EVER WILD
A Lifetime on Mount Adams

DARRYL LLOYD
Foreword by ROBERT MICHAEL PYLE

Darryl Lloyd

EVER WILD
A Lifetime on Mount Adams

DARRYL LLOYD
Foreword by ROBERT MICHAEL PYLE

Carpe Diem Books®

Portland, Oregon

Greg Highkin

*To past, present, and future field researchers of Mount Adams,
whose scientific studies question, provide knowledge, and enrich our world.*

Text and maps © 2018 by Darryl Lloyd
Photographs © 2018 by Darryl Lloyd, except as noted

First edition published 2018

ISBN: 978-0-9897104-9-7

Library of Congress Control Number 2018022380

Previously unpublished notes from Art Jones' 1923 Lookout Notebook used with permission of Ardith Thompson.

Editor: Tricia Brown
Designer: Kelley R. Dodd, KRD Design & Illustration
Cover Design: Elizabeth Watson, Watson Graphics
Mapmaker: Darryl Lloyd
Production Manager: Richard L. Owsiany, RLO Media Productions
Prepress: William Campbell, Mars Premedia

Carpe Diem Books®
*"Seize the Day—
Make the most of opportunities
with books!"*

Carpe Diem Books
8136 NW Skyline Boulevard
Portland, OR 97229
www.carpediembooks.com
www.mtadamsbook.com
503.936.6727
dick@carpediembooks.com

Printed in China

Caption, title page: Comet Hale-Bopp makes a spellbinding appearance in the night sky over Mount Adams in March 1997.
Caption, contents page: The author stands atop The Pinnacle (about 12,050 feet) in 1974, after a spring climb of Mount Adams' west ridge. In the background is Mount Rainier. (Darvel Lloyd)

Contents

At 12,276 feet, Mount Adams, or Pahto, rises as a noble sentinel to the south of Goat Rocks Wilderness.

The Mountain Loomed Above

When Darryl Lloyd refers to "a lifetime on Mount Adams," he's not fooling. As one who has always tried to hew to the landscapes around me and who most admires those who do, I was eager to read how my friend and consummate modern mountain-man Darryl Lloyd would bring such a life to print. And such a mountain!

I first met Darryl and Darvel Lloyd when they were running Flying L Ranch, near Glenwood, their magical childhood home and later guest ranch made and first managed by their parents. For years I taught butterfly and writing classes at the Flying L for the North Cascades Institute. From the Mardon skipper meadow outside the ranch house to the woodland paths where swallowtails dripped from Columbia lilies, this place was enchantment itself. But the Mountain loomed above, and the ranch was the launch-pad for trips to the Elysian Fields known as Bird Creek Meadows. Having the Lloyd Boys on hand to inform our impressions with their singular knowledge and experience of the place made our visits into rich expeditions.

Like the best outdoor lives, this one is more memoir of the place than the person. The author's own personal stories inform but do not eclipse the stories and faces of the actual place and its history, both natural and human, which are of course just different faces of the same coin with no clear edge between them. Darryl and his intimate mountain comrade (and twin brother), Darvel, have been physical, emotional, and intellectual denizens of the Mount Adams ecosystem since they were born in its beneficent shadow. No creatures occupy it with a better fit, and as I was not really surprised to discover, this extraordinary book shows just how such a fit was made.

Along the way, it paints a deep and rounded picture of the origins, ordeals (from eruption to sheep invasion to fire, with many stops in between), and order of business in the existence of this particular volcano. Past, present, and likely future, I've never felt better acquainted with a mountain, even its much-studied-and-reported neighbor, Mount St. Helens. Once I wanted to write a book called *Baker's Dozen*, which would profile each of the Cascade volcanoes as though through one long, personal, and twisty road-and-trail trip. But now I feel I could just leave out Mount Adams, as it's all been said already

Of course, each of the great Cascadian cones has had its able chroniclers: John Miles's great *Koma Kulshan* for Baker, Pat O'Hara and Tim McNulty's splendid *Realm of the Sleeping Giant* on Rainier, and so on. But I know of no other Cascadian writer-photographers who have made their mountain the central topic of their lives, as Darryl has with Adams; or who have achieved a portrait such as only that degree of extreme intimacy, mixed with powerful talents and dedication, could bring about. *Ever Wild* does just that. Darryl's photographs are as stunning as stunning can be, and his writing familiar and fleet-footed; together, they make a masterpiece.

From the Ridge of Wonders to Hellroaring Ridge and all the rest of the way around the mountain, Lloyd has long been striding that "high ridge" where, Vladimir Nabokov said, "the mountainside of 'scientific' knowledge joins the opposite slope of 'artistic' imagination"—and in this Book of Wonders, he takes us there. Combining his meticulous observations over the decades as master climber, fine naturalist, and dogged historian, with his exquisite and robust photography, he paints Mount Adams whole for both our hearts and our heads. And as the struggles continue to perpetuate the mountain's wildness against wrong-headed management and chance, even as glaciers melt and rock walls fall, he never lets us think for a minute that this volcano's future is a certainty. "I always hope for rolling back some of the harm that humans have done," he writes, and he is still working toward that goal. *Ever Wild* documents in fascinating detail the challenges that have been met, and those that remain.

From the shore of Takhlakh Lake, a grand view of the northwest face is one of the most impressive around the base of Mount Adams.

In the late sixties, I met and conversed with Supreme Court Justice William O. Douglas at a student conservation action to fight a mining threat to Glacier Peak in the North Cascades. One of my idols, along with Muir, Marsh, and Brower, Justice Douglas was a major force for wilderness protection throughout his long era on the Court, and off. His treasured time in the West was spent partly in Glenwood, where the Lloyd family became warm friends of his, including both the boys, well into their adulthood.

Of his many books, including *My Wilderness* with its Washington tales, Douglas's best-known title is *Of Men and Mountains*. When I think of the people especially identified with certain mountains—Humboldt and Chimborazo, Hillary and Everest, Harvey Manning and the North Cascades, for example—I can think of no one more twinned with a given peak than Darryl Lloyd and Mount Adams. And I think if his old friend Justice Bill could see this book, he'd say, "Yes—that's what I had in mind, when I spoke of men and mountains!"

—Robert Michael Pyle
Gray's River, Washington
April 2018

The bark and roots of western red cedar, "the tree of life," were vitally important to Native Americans on their annual migrations to the huckleberry fields of Mount Adams. Strips of the stringy cedar bark, as well as roots, were woven into baskets of many different designs and patterns.

Acknowledgments

First and foremost, I want to thank my dear brother Darvel. This book has been in the works for a long time, and Darv has stood by me through all the ups and downs. Without his endless patience, support, and assistance, the project might never have been completed.

During its earlier stages, portions of the manuscript were reviewed by a number of people who made invaluable edits and suggestions. Huge thanks go out to retired archaeologists Rick McClure and Cheryl Mack, volcanologist Wes Hildreth, research hydrologist Tom Pierson, marine geologist Rachel Haymon, glaciologist Andrew Fountain; advance editors Cloudy Sears and Erin Moore; author/poet Christine Colasurdo; and other writer friends including Ruth Kirk, Susan Saul, Hugh and Linda McMahan, and Susan Crowley. To all: Your advice and comments were immeasurably important, and I am very grateful for your time and efforts on this project.

I also want to acknowledge the board and many Friends of Mount Adams, who are dedicated and give financial assistance to protect and restore our great mountain. And thank you Julee Wasserman, proprietor of the Mt. Adams Lodge at the Flying L Ranch. Your gracious hospitality is very much appreciated whenever Darv and I pay a visit.

I am especially thankful to Ardith Thompson, who kindly provided stories and old black-and-white photos about her legendary father Art Jones, and who is featured in the chapter titled "The Summit Lookout."

My heartfelt thanks go out to my esteemed and longtime friend, Bob Pyle, for writing the Foreword. And to the book production team led by Dick Owsiany, with designers Betty Watson and Kelley Dodd, and William Campbell for all of his behind-the-scenes work. Finally, I can't express enough appreciation and gratitude to editor extraordinaire Tricia Brown, who is simply irreplaceable. And also to the whole team: Bless you all for bringing my words and images to light.

Twin lenticular clouds form over the southeast face as viewed from the Glenwood Valley.

Introduction

My love affair with all things Mount Adams in southern Washington began more than seventy years ago, when my twin brother Darvel and I first explored the trail around Bird Lake as two-year-olds.

We were raised in a large house at the foot of the mountain in a meadow near Glenwood. The house was designed by my grandfather and built by local carpenters, and almost every window framed Mount Adams. In clear weather, we couldn't help but watch the constantly changing light on its rugged southeast face. What a grand and sweeping view it was, with not a tree in the meadow to interrupt its broad and completely forested base.

Our family spent many summer days on Mount Adams, and we usually camped at the Forest Service showpiece campground at Bird Creek Meadows. One day Darvel and I got lost roaming the area off-trail by ourselves. We were about six years old at the time, and the area seemed to us like a maze of many small meadows, vales, low ridges, and streams that all looked alike. Toward sunset we found the trail and ran into worried adults out looking for us. The both of us have always remembered it fondly as an adventure. It would be the beginning of almost seven decades of off-trail ramblings by the Lloyd brothers on Mount Adams and in many other wild areas of the world.

Our deep involvement with the mountain has been almost continuous, from our 1940s childhood to the 1970s, when we founded and for ten years directed the Mount Adams Wilderness Institute (MAWI), to the present. We've observed profound physical changes on Mount Adams and played different roles in imparting a greater understanding and appreciation of it. We've advocated its protection for a half-century. It's been an exhilarating odyssey of love for a place. And as elders, our association with the great volcano continues to enrich, always a learning experience. I can't imagine a life without Mount Adams, and on clear days, I still view it from my front window in Hood River, Oregon.

Darvel and I look back and marvel at how the best parts of Mount Adams have remained essentially wild and pristine through the decades of our ramblings. In the year that we were born, 1942, the chief of the U.S. Forest Service designated Mount Adams a "Wild Area" of 42,411 acres. Its boundary, which would change three times in the following decades, reached as low as 4,000 feet and included the wondrous eastern flanks. Forest Service management centered on providing "a wilderness experience to all who wish to enjoy it."

Eight famous words from Henry David Thoreau's 1854 *Walden*—"In wildness is the preservation of the world"—led to Congress passing the Wilderness Act of 1964, which permanently protected 9.1 million acres of national forest lands in thirteen western states. The Mount Adams Wilderness, along with Goat Rocks and Glacier Peak, were the first three in Washington to be included in the original Act. Today the system contains more than seven hundred fifty wilderness areas totaling more than one hundred ten million acres from coast to coast—within national parks, national forests, national wildlife refuges, and Bureau of Land Management lands.

Still, Mount Adams remained little understood, "overlooked" for many years. Here stands one of the great ice-covered sentinels in the Cascade Range. At 12,276 feet, it is the second-highest peak in the Pacific Northwest, exceeded only by world-famous Mount Rainier. Dominating a vast region of the Columbia River, the volcano towers two miles above the valleys of southern Washington and covers more than two hundred thirty square miles. Its massive, glaciated bulk is prominent on the horizons of population centers in two states and visible from as far away as 155 miles in the Blue Mountains of northeastern Oregon. Sacred to Native Americans across the millennia, Adams is also called Pahto by the Yakama Nation, but scholars like anthropologist Eugene Hunn use the name *Pátu*, meaning "snow-topped mountain." Much of the volcano is now protected as designated national forest wilderness or by primitive area steward-ship by the Yakama Nation.

With an eruptive volume of about forty-eight cubic miles, Mount Adams ranks among the most prominent of the world's stratovolcanoes. Its lava flows, old and new, would cover Manhattan Island three miles deep. In the Cascades only Mount Shasta in northern California has greater volume. Mount Rainier is 2,100 feet higher and much bulkier above timberline; but because Rainier is perched on a non-volcanic pedestal, its eruptive volume is only about two-thirds that of Adams. Oregon's highest peak, Mount Hood, is a thousand feet lower than Mount Adams and by volume just one-fourth as large.

The true character of Mount Adams cannot be fully appreciated without circling and observing the whole mountain. It's a changing landscape of magnificent, unspoiled beauty. At least eight rugged faces are revealed, and no two are alike. The incomparable east face is distinguished by five glaciers, three great ridges, and some of the wildest precipices in the Cascades. The heavily glaciated northern faces are more rounded in appearance and claim the most spectacular icefalls. On the west and southwest faces, multiple summits rise steeply above smaller cirque glaciers and avalanche cliffs. The relatively narrow south side—the only face on the mountain shaped like a volcanic cone—is characterized by a series of long, low-angle ridges with several rapidly diminishing glaciers.

Mount Adams is world-class in more ways than eruptive volume or sheer grandeur. Six ecological regions have been mapped at different elevations and sides of the mountain, and more than eight hundred forty species of plants have been documented above the 4,000-foot elevation. Exquisite parklands near timberline are ripe in summer with lush, flower-filled meadows, cascading streams, and shimmering lakes. Expanses of ground-hugging alpine tundra above timberline provide important habitat for miniature plants, mountain goats, small mammals, and birds.

The broad forested belt—fragmented by logging, fires, and insect mortality—harbors bear, elk, cougars, lynx, pine marten, and more elusive carnivores that include wolverine, Cascade red fox, and wolf. There are still hidden lakes without names or trails leading to them. Deep, glacier-carved valleys on the eastern and western flanks have waterfalls and swamps that are virtually unexplored.

From Mount Adams, dozens of vigorous streams drain radially in all directions. Twelve glaciers, many permanent snow fields and countless springs feed four rivers that flow into the Columbia River: Klickitat to the east, White Salmon to the south, Lewis to the west, and Cispus (which feeds the Cowlitz) to the north.

Such a magnificent mountain should have gained national recognition long ago. Yet it remained overshadowed in attention and popularity by neighboring rivals, Mounts Hood, St. Helens, and Rainier. Roads to these three more popular volcanoes were far better a century ago than they are today on Mount Adams. People who love the *wildness* of the mountain aren't complaining, though. We know that fewer visitors help keep it wild. Even today, many of us simply stay away from the one route that is popular—the South Spur or "South Climb"—where each summer thousands gather to "bag" a relatively easy summit. Perhaps *Ever Wild* will inspire climbers to better appreciate Mount Adams' massiveness, complexity, and splendor.

Despite its rank as first in volume and second in height among all stratovolcanoes in the Cascades of Washington and Oregon, Mount Adams has taken a backseat to many other Northwest mountains in terms of recognition and protection as a whole. Never has there been a full-size book devoted to the diverse character and uniqueness of Mount Adams. Most only know bits and pieces of its fascinating human and natural history. I hope these pages, written and visual, will fill important gaps in the knowledge and beauty of the colossus of southern Washington.

Top: From the Selah and Yakima valleys, Mount Adams' exceptionally broad east face is unique among all Cascade volcanoes. *Above:* The sprawling, multi-summit Mount Adams dominates the eastern horizon from Mount St. Helens.

PART ONE

PEOPLE OF THE MOUNTAIN

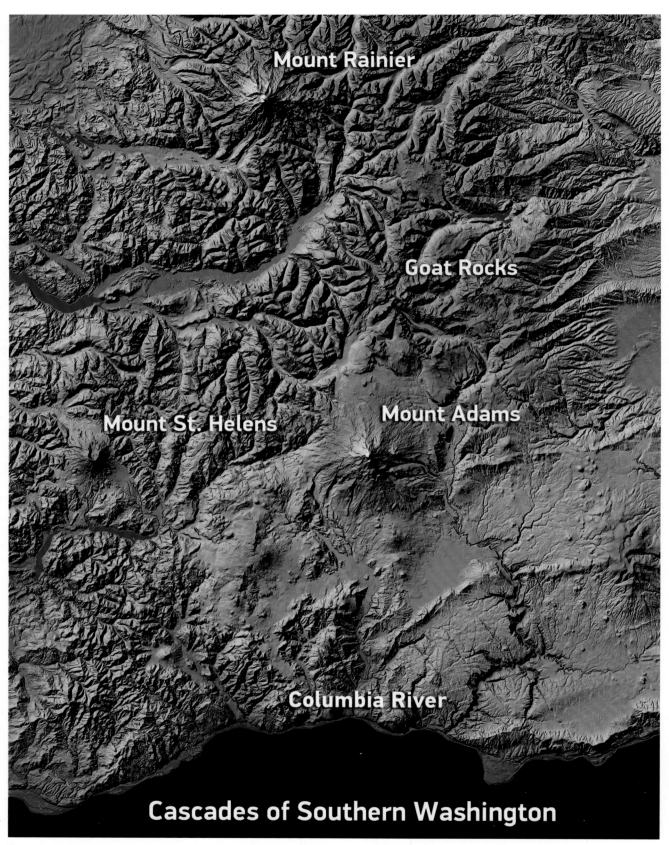

Cascades of Southern Washington

Towering two miles above the valleys at its base, Mount Adams dominates the Cascades of southern Washington and covers more than two hundred thirty square miles. Its huge eruptive volume is estimated at forty-eight cubic miles. (U.S. Geological Survey)

Chapter 1

Overlooked Giant of the Cascades

A great mountain is like a great poem. At first acquaintance our minds have not the power to grasp its full magnificence. But as we know it day by day and year by year new beauties unfold, new grandeurs appear, as our senses develop new powers to understand and to measure, until, at last if our minds be great enough to comprehend, it finally stands forth in all its sublimity.

— C. E. Rusk

With a few notable exceptions in early literature, Mount Adams was never given the stature it deserved. In 1919, Claude Ewing Rusk wrote a booklet titled *Mount Adams, Towering Sentinel of the Lower Columbia Basin*, offering supporting reasons for national park status. His popular book, *Tales of a Western Mountaineer*, released in 1924 and reprinted in 1978, championed the mountain's greatness, echoing Theodore Winthrop's mid-nineteenth century claim that Mount Adams was "noble enough to be the pride of a continent." But Rusk also lamented the neglect that the mountain had received for so many years.

The stage for two centuries of indifference may have been set on October 19, 1805, when Lewis and Clark mistook Mount Adams for Mount St. Helens. Looking west from a cliff above the Columbia River near present-day Umatilla, Captain William Clark noted in his journal (original spelling): "I discovered a high mountain of emence hight covered with Snow . . . I take it to be Mt. St. Helens . . ." On the expedition's return the following spring, both Adams and St. Helens were visible from a closer vantage point. Camping near the mouth of the Willamette River on April 2, 1806, Clark noted ". . . a high humped Mountain to the East of Mt St Helians."

It wasn't only Lewis and Clark who mistook the two mountains. Topographers continued to confuse the identities of the two volcanoes throughout the first half of the nineteenth century, though it's hard to believe how anyone could mistake the Fuji-like cone of Mount St. Helens with the sprawling, multi-summit Mount Adams

thirty-four miles to the east. Adams exceeds St. Helens in elevation by more than 2,700 feet and is vastly larger in bulk.

In the early 1800s, Hudson's Bay Company trappers and traders, accompanied by Indian guides, penetrated the forested wilderness of lesser mountains between Adams and St. Helens. From ridges and hilltops, the two highest peaks in southern Washington dominated the horizon and played a prominent role in Native cultures. Yet Mount Adams remained a mystery to non-indigenous people, because there were no written accounts of the area until well after the mid-nineteenth century.

It was not a mystery to Pacific Northwest tribes on both sides of the Columbia River, who had for millennia witnessed eruptions of the St. Helens, Adams, and Hood volcanoes (referred to as the "Guardians of the Columbia" in John Williams' popular 1912 book). Legends explaining the mountains' origins were passed down orally from generation to generation and survive to this day. Well-worn ancient trails led to all sides of Mount Adams, and for thousands of years, large groups of Indians trekked to the high country for food and necessities.

The name *Pátu* eminently deserved to be on nineteenth-century Anglo-American maps, but early geographers rarely considered Native names for great peaks of the West that Euro-Americans claimed they'd discovered. Tahoma (or Tacoma) for Mount Rainier might have been one of the few exceptions, but unfortunately the Native name didn't stick.

Mount Adams boldly stands about fifty miles south of famous Mount Rainier, the granddaddy of all stratovolcanoes within the United States. (Les Lloyd Collection)

In 1826, Canadian explorer David Thompson produced a rare map of western North America that showed a large peak (Adams) in a range of lower hills north of the Columbia River and the town of The Dalles. The mountain was positioned correctly in latitude and was labeled simply as "Mount." When Thompson explored the Columbia River, the conical south face of Mount Adams would have been prominent from the bluff above the town. Sadly, it was a missed opportunity for Thompson to learn the Indian name of the mountain and put it on the map.

Compounding the white man's confusion about the existence of Mount Adams was a muddled effort in the early 1840s for the Cascade volcanoes to be named after former U.S. presidents. It was a scheme devised by Bostonian author Hall J. Kelley, who renamed Mount Hood as Mount Adams after the second president, John Adams. Kelley knew nothing of the great *Pátu* north of the Columbia River. In his 1839 memoir, he wrote:

"These isolated and remarkable cones, which are now called among the hunters of the Hudson's Bay Company by other names, I have christened after our ex-Presidents, viz.: 1. Washington [St. Helens], latitude 46 deg. 15 min.; 2. Adams [actually Hood], latitude 45 deg. 10 min."

Navy Lieutenant Charles Wilkes, the first American to chronicle Mount Rainier in 1841, went on to describe Mount Adams to the south and named it "Mt. Hudson." Wilkes wrote: " . . . another snowy peak visible from the plain very much resembling Mt. Rainier. It appears Eastward of the Range. Not being represented on my chart I called it Mt. Hudson after the commander of the *Peacock*." Lieutenant Wilkes and Lieutenant William L. Hudson commanded ships in the four-year-long Wilkes Expedition that explored the Pacific Ocean and surrounding lands. His surveys included the Columbia River as far as Fort Walla Walla, but his maps failed to show any mark of the peak that resembled Rainier. The name "Mount Hudson" faded away into obscurity.

A few years later, in 1843, New Englander and author Thomas J. Farnham attempted to implement Hall J. Kelley's "President's Range" plan. However his knowledge of the region's geography was even worse than Kelley's. In a book about his grim Oregon Trail journey, Farnham wrote: "Mount Adams lies under the parallel of forty-five degrees, about twenty-five miles north of the cascades of the Columbia. This is one of the finest peaks of the chain, clad with eternal snows, five thousand feet down its sides." Farnham may have intended the new name for Mount St. Helens, assuming his "cascades" were located at today's Bridge of the Gods. But the 45th parallel was long known to pass through northern Oregon. As it turned out, the name Mount Adams stuck to the far more massive and higher volcano (*Pátu*) that towered nowhere near the location that Farnham described.

The first published map that correctly positioned Mount Adams was made in 1853–54 by Captain George McClellan's Pacific Railroad Survey expedition. McClellan's job was to scout a route for the first part of a transcontinental railroad. It was a large expedition consisting of sixty-one men, one hundred sixty horses and mules, three hunters, fifteen non-Native guides, and twenty-nine soldiers. Using Native guides, his expedition in August 1853 followed an old Indian route, then called the Klickitat Trail. Their route passed through the present-day Trout Lake Valley and eastward along the southern edge of "Tahk Plain" (later named Camas Prairie and Glenwood Valley). Topographer John Lambert added notes about the terrain, but gave no estimates of elevations.

During the same month, August 1853, author and traveler Theodore Winthrop spotted and identified Mount Adams from mountainous country toward the northeast. Winthrop wrote in his popular book *Canoe and Saddle*: "Mount Adams, Tacoma the Less, was the first object to cleave the darkness. I looked westward, and saw a sunlit mass of white, high up among the black clouds, and baseless but for them." Winthrop ended the paragraph with: " . . . these noble isolated snow-peaks are to a traveller memorials on the land he has left, or beacons, firmer than a pillar of cloud, of a land whither he goes." At the time Winthrop was traveling on horseback, with a Yakama Indian guide, from Puget Sound to Fort Dalles. He then took a wagon train heading east toward his home state

of New York, and soon afterward, in 1861, died fighting in the Civil War.

Most historians agree that the first white men to climb Mount Adams made up a party of four surveyors, including A. G. Aiken, who made an ascent in 1854. Most likely they chose the North Cleaver as their route. The surveyors were planning a military road on the north side of Adams that would eventually connect the Columbia River to Puget Sound via Naches Pass. Not until 1864 did anyone attempt the south side. Groups of up to six men and women, including an Indian guide, would leave White Salmon by horseback and ride through Camas Prairie to reach the mountain. One larger party in an 1867 ascent claimed the summit stood at "14,000 feet above the level of the sea."

The first reasonably accurate measurement of Mount Adams' elevation wasn't made until 1883, when R. Goode's Northern Pacific Transcontinental Geological Survey established its height at 12,300 feet. In that same year, an *Oregonian* story was likely the first published "examination" of an unnamed glacier (Mazama) on Mount Adams. Members of the party were frightened by the crevasses: "The terrific pressure behind and the unyielding stone wall in front, have cracked the glacier into huge chasms longitudinally to the movement of the mass. We looked with horror into green, slippery walled fissures of unknown depth."

The earliest published photos of Mount Adams came a few years later, appearing in 1886 in a Portland publication, *The West Shore*. In the accompanying article, Professor William D. Lyman of Whitman College incorrectly hypothesized that Mount Adams volcano was one hundred miles wide and the source of vast basalt flows in southern Washington. Lyman described six glaciers on Mount Adams: "one on Bacon Creek [Hellroaring Creek], one on White Salmon River, one on Lewis River, and three on different forks of the Klickitat River." Within a year or so, sheepherders named three of the glaciers: White Salmon, "Hell-Roaring" (later renamed Mazama), and Klickitat.

Mount Adams played second fiddle in prominence at least through the end of the 1800s, when "the geographies and the reference books" listed its height at 9,570 feet. As late as 1924, C. E. Rusk noted that some books "even to this day perpetuate the old slander, and persist

The first rays of sunlight bathe the southeast face on a bitterly cold January morning. I shot this from the deck of my former home, adjacent to the Flying L Ranch near Glenwood.

in reiterating the stereotyped figures [9,570 feet]." This astounding error originated from topographers thinking Adams (12,276 feet) and St. Helens (9,677 feet) were about equal in height. Both mountains revealed about one-mile-vertical extents of snow, rock, and ice. But the uppermost elevation of tree growth on St. Helens is limited by recent explosive eruptions and pyroclastic flows; on Mount Adams, timberline elevation is governed by climate, aspect, and other factors such as soil conditions and recent glaciation.

Bounded by the Yakama Reservation to the east, Mount Adams stands alone in an unpopulated part of Washington. The great mountain dominates the communities of Trout Lake and Glenwood, which occupy valleys on its south and southeast sides. Each community has slightly fewer than five hundred residents, and most

are engaged in logging and agriculture. Only a few businesses are connected with tourist activities that focus on the mountain.

Much of the lower eastern flanks of Mount Adams are within the closed part of the Yakama Reservation, which is off-limits to all but tribal members. Permission to enter is rarely granted. The Yakama Nation Mount Adams Recreation Area (also called "Tract D") occupies a splendid corner of the mountain on its east and southeast sides.

Historically both the Forest Service and Yakama Nation have somewhat limited the mountain's recreational use, because of its geographic isolation, wilderness or primitive-use management, and road access. However, growing numbers of climbers, day hikers, and other recreationists have created the need for plans to further protect the "overlooked giant."

Chapter 2

First People

Every part of this Earth is sacred to my people. Every shining pine needle, every sandy shore, every mist in the dark woods. Every clearing, and humming insect is Holy in the memory and the experience of my people.

— Chief Seattle

Native Americans have hunted and gathered food and other necessities on Mount Adams for more than seven thousand years. Ancient use is supported by archaeological evidence that includes charred huckleberry fruits, nearly as old, on at least one site north of Mount Adams, as stone projectile points found high on the mountain.

Climate change was likely an important factor in drawing the earliest people to Mount Adams country. A relatively warm and dry period in the West, called the *Altithermal*, occurred between 7,500 and 5,000 years ago, and evidence from that time points to large, semi-permanent settlements along some river valleys leading up to the mountain. Seasonal campsites were scattered around the high country; artifacts were found at many sites up to 6,000 feet and higher. Cheryl Mack and Rick McClure of Trout Lake—married and now retired career archaeologists for Gifford Pinchot National Forest—analyzed many of those finds while remaining cautious about sharing specific site locations.

High in the Goat Rocks, twenty miles north of Mount Adams, archaeologists investigated a rare obsidian quarry for stone tool manufacturing, first discovered by William O. Douglas in 1915. Carbon dating of charcoal fragments indicates the site was in use about 6,260 years ago. Tools fashioned there were then transported to seasonal encampments throughout the upper Cowlitz River drainage. In the late 1980s, a Forest Service field crew discovered a chalcedony (type of quartz) quarry near Council Lake a few miles northwest of Mount Adams. The quarry, documented and recorded by McClure, was

apparently an additional source of hard stone used for tool-making by early Indians.

Native hunters made projectile points and stone knives near the base of Mount Adams to target and kill prey much higher on the mountain's slopes. In 1977 one of our Wilderness Institute participants found an artifact on the north shoulder of Mount Adams at around 7,300 feet. After examining my photograph, both Mack and McClure agreed it was likely the tip of a thrusting spear or hafted knife, used to dispatch a wounded mountain goat. Its function and age were difficult to determine from a photo, McClure said, adding they would need to examine the artifact for use-wear patterns and other characteristics. Mack believed the point was made from a bifacial blank of high-quality chert or another microcrystalline silicate. Her team had found a very similar thrusting spear point—most likely used to hunt bear—in a cave elsewhere within the Gifford Pinchot National Forest. One beautiful point photographed in their collection was dated at 9,700 years old.

In 2008 McClure found a broken projectile point at the 10,900-foot level on Suksdorf Ridge of Mount Adams. The artifact is the highest archaeological discovery made in Washington up to 2018. One wonders if the hunter was chasing a mountain goat. This amazing find convinces me that the first person to climb Mount Adams was probably a Native American hunter of long ago. The urge seems eternal for certain hardy, inquisitive people of *any* race to scramble higher and higher on prominent peaks such as Adams, and then go for the summit. Perhaps two bull

"Autumn in the Berry Fields" is part of a much larger mural on a building in Toppenish, Washington. Painted by Janet Essley, this scene shows a Yakama Nation family collecting and drying huckleberries, with a variety of basket types that were used for different purposes. In the background is Mount Adams.

elk that I saw near the top of Mount Adams in the mid-1970s had that same instinct.

Native Americans traveled in large numbers to the mountain until the end of the nineteenth century, when sheep came to dominate all flanks of Mount Adams. The indigenous people would gather basketry materials (cedar bark, etc.), dig roots, pick huckleberries, fish, and hunt game. Large mammals, including deer, bear, elk, and mountain goat, were important to the early peoples' survival. Mountain goats were especially prized for their meat, wool, horns, and hooves.

This pattern of Native use in the Mount Adams high country had been repeated over the millennia. Certainly, events like wildfires, climate fluctuations, and volcanic eruptions would have caused interruptions. Lava flows accompanied by light ashfall erupted from ten flank vents on Mount Adams between about 7,700 and 1,000 years ago. A small steam explosion on the summit occurred about five thousand years ago. While active lava flows would have disrupted Native use and travel on the mountain, dormant periods between eruptions lasted far longer. The jagged, dark andesite lava flows—up to eighty feet high and nearly seven miles long—forced long detours in Native travel routes from one side of the mountain to another. On the northeast side, early people on foot or horseback had

to climb almost to 8,000 feet to safely skirt the extensive Muddy Fork lava flow and much larger glaciers during the Little Ice Age.

Far bigger and more frequent explosive eruptions of Mount St. Helens were orders of magnitude more lethal and disruptive than any post-Ice Age volcanic event on Mount Adams. The Smith Creek Eruptive Period from 3,900 to 3,300 years ago created severe interruptions to Native use of the upper Cowlitz and Lewis River watersheds, and probably kept Indians completely off Mount Adams for decades. Mount St. Helens eruptions that greatly exceeded the volume of the 1980 event continued intermittently through the 1700s, but dormant periods of as long as several hundred years would have allowed access to Mount Adams from the west and north.

A peril far worse than volcanic eruptions faced tribal populations when the first white explorers and fur traders made their way into the region. In the late 1700s and early 1800s, deadly diseases such as smallpox, influenza, and "fever and ague" (malaria) were accidentally introduced. It is truly a horrible and tragic story. The Natives had no immunity, and by 1840 these diseases had wiped out roughly 65 to 95 percent of Northwest Indian populations, according to the University of Washington's Center for the Study of the Pacific Northwest.

Left: A Native American woman dries huckleberries on banks sloped toward a smoldering fire. Known as *wiwnu* to the Yakamas, huckleberries were a sacred food. (U.S. Forest Service) *Right:* A billy mountain goat in alpine habitat on the north side would have been a prime target for early Native hunters.

Indians closest to Mount Adams belonged to the Yakama and Klickitat tribes to the east and south. They lived primarily along the Yakima, Klickitat, and White Salmon rivers, and spoke the Sahaptin language of the Columbia Plateau. The Yakamas called the mountain Pahto (also *Pátu*), and considered it sacred as a symbol of continuity and a source of prosperity. Columbia River tribes downriver of Celilo also shared the mountain. They spoke a Chinookan language, but each language had its subdivisions. Klickitat is another name given to Mount Adams, derived from the Chinook word meaning "beyond," such as "beyond the Cascade Mountains." The Wishram and Cascades tribes made regular trips to Mount Adams, as did the Cowlitz and Taidnapam people coming in from the north and west. The various tribes traded food and other items in a widespread subsistence network.

The coming of horses to Native Americans on the Columbia Plateau, beginning in the early 1700s, made it possible for groups of up to several hundred people at a time to reach the huckleberry fields in only a few days of travel time. And in late summer, tribes from all over southern Washington and northern Oregon converged on *Pátu* to harvest berries. Of the twelve species of huckleberries in the Cascade Range, the most highly prized was then and still is *Vaccinium membranaceum*—renowned for its large, sweet, dark-blue fruit. Known as *wiwnu* to the Yakamas, huckleberries were a sacred food, and according

to oral tradition, had great power for doing good. These seasonal gatherings, called *wiwnumi* ("berry month") were eagerly anticipated as a time for socializing and trading, as well as subsistence food-gathering. Indians believed that as long as respect was shown for *wiwnu*, the berries would return each year to fill the winter stores. The elders spent many hours storytelling with younger people, as they passed on essential information on how to preserve the berry fields, their traditions, and nomadic way of life.

American Indians used fire for centuries as a tool to increase huckleberry production, according to research by Cheryl Mack. Repeated fires reduced the invasion of shrubs and trees, and were set in autumn after berry harvest. Natives knew that huckleberries need sunlight to produce a full crop of fruit. The burns also created grassy meadows for horses to graze and to draw deer and elk within easy range of the hunters.

The earliest account of a large Indian berry-picking expedition on Mount Adams was written in August 1878 by Francis Marion Streamer, a lonely white man invited along by the Indians. He was a newspaperman, who had trekked to the town of The Dalles from his original home in Chicago to Seattle two years earlier. The huckleberry expedition consisted of a tribal party from the Simcoes in eastern Klickitat County. With some two hundred horses, they started at The Dalles and rode for days, following well-established trails to *Ollalie*, or "huckleberry country"

A Native American man picks berries and carries intricately patterned baskets woven from beargrass leaves and western redcedar bark. (U.S. Forest Service)

Other tribal groups gathered in the area. According to Streamer's account, a typical campsite bustled with nearly two hundred Native Americans and more than a thousand ponies grazing nearby. The Indians' diet in camp included huckleberries in every form—mashed, fried in salmon oil, fried in pancakes—plus salmon, trout, roasted squirrels, and bread. Streamer described a dessert of "wild spinach" (called *malyak*), which was boiled in water with flour, sugar, and camas. In camp, they dried many bushels of berries on sloped banks facing smoldering log fires. Dried berries were then stored in tub-shaped cedar-bark baskets.

Streamer spent hours watching the men gamble, play cards, and play their traditional stick-and-bone games (*palyúut*). They bet large quantities of blankets and even clothes. He estimated that nearly a half-ton of dried and fresh berries were transported back to The Dalles on their return trip. The berries would become a food staple and trading commodity for the coming year.

The Klickitat Indians were fond of salmon-huckleberry pemmican, made from smoked and dried salmon. Salmon was pounded into paste and then mixed with dried berries and certain roots like camas. McClellan's expedition in 1853 reported that the Yakamas made use of some twenty-three kinds of roots and eighteen kinds of berries.

Gathering materials for baskets was a top priority for Indians on their annual migrations to the berry fields. The main materials were beargrass leaves (*Xerophyllum tenax*) and the stringy bark and roots of western redcedar (*Thuja plicata*), which were plentiful along their routes. Leaves of beargrass, called *yai*, were coiled and closely interwoven with strips of cedar bark and cedar roots. Natural dyes were also collected and used for intricate, geometric designs woven into the baskets. The process took much labor, patience, and skill. Cooking vessels, pouches, cups, and even hats were constructed from the same materials. Vessels were watertight and richly ornamental. They are functional to this day and in high demand by collectors and museums. Passed down from my parents, a large Klickitat basket of unknown date is perfect for holding maps that I use frequently.

The simplest type of utilitarian basket, not watertight, was constructed completely from bark that was stripped from a western redcedar tree. In the 1930s, Art Jones of

on the northwest flanks of Mount Adams. Their route passed through Camas Prairie and upper Trout Lake Valley and crossed the White Salmon River before it traversed the western half of the mountain at the subalpine level. The "pleasant journey," as Streamer called it, likely passed Lookingglass Lake ("one small lake"), and the high point was probably around 6,200 feet on Crofton Ridge. This ancient Native American route would become part of the modern "Round-the-Mountain Trail" of the 1950s and early 1960s.

Streamer described their destination as "near the Lake on the Summit of the Cascades." The name of the lake is not known for sure, but it was probably somewhere in the triangle of Ollalie Lake, Chain-of-Lakes, and Takhlakh Lake. He wrote, "We have a very pretty place to camp in full view of Mount Adams, surrounded by huckleberries and strawberries of all sizes."

Above left: A stone point found at 7,300 feet on the north side was likely the tip of a thrusting spear or hafted knife, used to dispatch a wounded mountain goat. *Above:* Natives have long used beargrass leaves to weave baskets, while its fibers were used for clothing. Rhizomes were roasted and eaten.

Trout Lake made the one I now own. It is a cylindrical sleeve of cedar bark: rough on the outside, smooth on the inside, and curved at the bottom. The cylinder is laced with cedar strips up each side and woven together around the top.

Camas roots (or bulbs) were one of the most important food staples of indigenous people near Mount Adams and elsewhere. The beautiful, blue lily (*Camassia quamash*) bloomed in mid-elevation meadows and prairies at the foot of the mountain, especially in Camas Prairie. Native Americans pronounced it *kamass* or *quamash*, depending on the tribe. The Yakama and Klickitat word for camas is *wák'amu.* Using pointed digging sticks with antler handles, early Indians usually dug the bulbs after flowering in July. Bulbs were then grilled or boiled. The surplus that people couldn't eat immediately was ground to paste, then shaped into little loaves and cooked a second time into a form of camas bread, which would stay wholesome for weeks. The whole, cleaned starch-rich camas bulbs were preserved by smoking or sun-drying. In this form they were highly valued for trading or given as gifts. Even today camas roots are eaten at ceremonial First Foods feasts, such as at Celilo village.

The roots were harvested for thousands of years in Camas Prairie, long before non-Native settlers moved in with their plows and domesticated animals. The first white explorers named the valley Takh Plain. (*Taák* literally means "meadow" in the Sahaptin language.) Dense patches of blue camas still bloom every May or June on the southern edges of the valley. A different species, *Camassia quamish breviflora,* is found at 4,400 feet in Muddy Meadows on the north side of Mount Adams. Years ago *Camassia breviflora* might also have bloomed in Takh Takh Meadow at nearly the same elevation on the northwest side.

In August 1869, two young Yakama Tribe members named Abe Lincoln and Charley Olney wanted to pay a visit to their people camping in the great huckleberry fields on Mount Adams' northwest side. An accident while crossing a glacier resulted in an unusual survival story of bravery and heroism, documented by C. E. Rusk in the 1946 *American Alpine Journal.*

Starting their journey from the Yakima Valley and riding racehorses, Lincoln and Olney made rapid progress. They forded the Klickitat River and by mid-afternoon were high on the mountain's northeast flank in Devils Gardens. Instead of following a well-traveled Indian route

For thousands of years, Natives have harvested *Camassia quamash* for its roots. Dense patches still flourish in Camas Prairie.

across that side of the mountain (today called the Highline Trail), Lincoln decided to take a shortcut across the lower part of the Lyman Glacier, which was vastly larger and thicker in 1869 than it is today. His friend Olney reluctantly followed. As Lincoln foolishly rode across a crevasse on a "snow bridge," the icy bridge collapsed and both horse and rider plunged between thirty and fifty feet into the abyss. Although his horse died immediately, Lincoln was only bruised but extremely frightened, wedged in as he was on top of his dead horse. Olney attempted to haul Lincoln out with a spare rope, but the rope hung up on the lip of the crevasse. He then had no choice but to head down the mountain for help—the closest being the huckleberry encampment at least twelve miles away and about 3,500 feet lower in elevation.

Olney rode all night, finally reaching his relatives' camp about nine the following morning. A party of thirteen hardy men with five horses quickly set out for the rescue. Over difficult glacial till and lava terrain, they reached the scene of the accident about noon. Lincoln was

alive but extremely weak after twenty-one hours of waiting deep inside the frigid crevasse. His rescuers lowered two ropes with rawhide lariat loops. Lincoln managed to place the loops around his upper body, while the men on top lined the lip of the crevasse with blankets. They hauled him up almost within their reach, grabbed him by the hair and dragged him over the crevasse lip onto the glacier surface. After two hours of rest and food, Lincoln finally regained his body heat, and the party slowly rode and walked back to the huckleberry camp.

Abe Lincoln was a very lucky and a very tough young man. The two men were not mountaineers and they never intended to be. And they never forgot the lessons of that day. Fifty-two years later, Lincoln was an elder living in the Yakima Valley when he heard about C. E. Rusk's plan to lead the new Cascadians club outing to "ramble over the big glaciers" and climb Mount Adams. Rusk retold Abe Lincoln's response in his article in the *American Alpine Journal*: "The Cascadians are fools," he said. "I know they are fools—I've been there, I know!"

Chapter 3

The Great Sheep Invasions

The welfare of sheep depends solely upon the care they get from their shepherd. Therefore, the better the shepherd, the healthier the sheep.

— Kay Arthur

The era of massive sheep grazing on Mount Adams began in 1886 and lasted until the early 1970s. Except for logging on the mountain's lower slopes, no human-managed activity had a more profound negative impact on the area's ecology. Yet published information about the effects of grazing on Adams is meager. Many stories of the huge sheep invasions have been carried to the grave by the men who could tell them best.

Not only sheep, but fire played a role, and the two were connected. Wildfires during the last half of the 1800s created an abundance of meadows in the forests that encircled Mount Adams. "The Great Conflagration of 1885" burned three-quarters of a township on the south and southeast flanks, "where stood the dense forests," according to old field notes preserved by the Forest Service. C. E. Rusk wrote about "terrific conflagrations" in the fall of 1895 sweeping through timbered sections on the northern slopes of the mountain. In 1899, Fred Plummer mapped vast burned areas in the south Cascades in color. His map was the first federal map of the Mount Rainier Forest Reserve that also included most of Mount Adams. In his written report, Plummer mentioned that Indians and sheepherders started fires to promote the growth of huckleberries and grass.

On the mountain's lower, southern slopes, more frequent low-severity fires—sparked by both lightning and man—produced park-like forests dominated by mature ponderosa pines and Douglas fir. In 1875, Henry F. Suksdorf was among a climbing party that followed an Indian trail above Trout Lake Valley. In a letter to the *Oregonian* newspaper, he described gradually ascending "through splendid forests interspersed with pastures of luxuriant and nutritious grass, waiting for herds of sheep and cattle to grow fat on it." Subalpine meadows higher on the south side—eventually called Bird Creek Meadows—were described in an August 30, 1883, *Daily Oregonian* article as "beautiful and brilliant parks [that] vary in size from twenty to two hundred acres, but larger ones [are] lower down." Sheepherders found the gorgeous parkland a few years later, and called it Happy Valley.

Word of the seemingly endless grass-filled meadows spread rapidly throughout sheep-ranching country of Washington and Oregon. Most of the slopes encircling Mount Adams were public domain, and grazing was unregulated, free for the taking. In 1886 the first band of five thousand sheep arrived from the John Day Valley of central Oregon. Other bands followed, coming in from north-central Oregon. It was like a gold rush: the great sheep invasion was on.

By the late 1880s, bands as large as ten thousand animals—"grass-eating woolly hordes" as described by Robert Ballou in *Early Klickitat Valley Days*—were driven to Mount Adams from throughout Klickitat and Yakima counties. Oregon ranchers transported an estimated sixty-three thousand sheep by ferries at The Dalles and followed different routes to the mountain. Most passed through Camas Prairie (Glenwood Valley) on the southeast side of Adams. Sheepherders were "literally in a race . . . to get the best grass first," said Rick McClure, former archaeologist at the Gifford Pinchot National Forest. Bands of sheep "often arrived too early, destroying the new forage crop before it could be safely grazed."

The Bird Creek Meadows, originally called Happy Valley, were much larger when photographed in 1901 (top) than in 2014. In the mid-1880s, word spread of the endless, grass-filled meadows; the great sheep invasion began and continued like the gold rush. (Top: Harry F. Reid, National Snow and Ice Data Center)

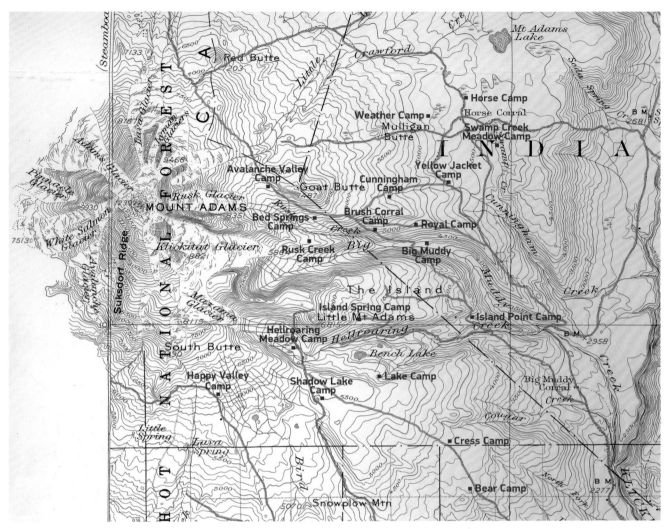

Old-timer Leonard Rolph helped identify old sheepherder camps and trails on the east side, as shown on a portion of a 1904 USGS thirty-minute quadrangle. Native Americans on horseback had used the trails since the early 1700s, when horses first arrived on the Columbia Plateau.

At the turn of the century, the sheep numbers were staggering. Forest Service and Washington Sheep Commissioner reports indicate that upwards of one hundred fifty thousand woolly domestics were brought to Mount Adams annually for unregulated grazing. According to Cheryl Mack, the real numbers were actually higher than that, based on 1901 permits issued on Mount Rainier Forest Preserve for a quarter-million sheep. When the Forest Service was established in 1905, a report to then-Forest Service Chief Gifford Pinchot framed the issue as the biggest problem facing management of the forest reserves at the time.

Filibert Roth's 1901 federal study *Grazing in the Forest Reserves* described the damage to mountain meadows.

Everything was destroyed in the sheep-bedding grounds, where herders returned to the same campsite year after year and to the same camp on a daily basis. Sheep trails used every year, Roth wrote, "have the appearance of a much-traveled road. Small vegetation is destroyed and the ground is worn into numerous rut-like trails . . . commonly 50-100 yards in width." A grazing report for the Mount Adams area stated that sheepmen had habits of camping for several weeks at one place where water and horse feed were handy. This caused the range to be tramped out for quite a distance in all directions from the camp.

Before the sheep invasions, pioneer botanist Wilhelm Suksdorf spent about a dozen halcyon years collecting plant samples on the southeast side of Mount Adams.

In 1910, the Gotchen Guard Station was built as an entry point for all sheep bands coming to the mountain. Rangers on horseback enforced grazing allotments. (U.S. Forest Service)

His brother Theodore described some of the impacts that Wilhelm experienced in the years that followed: "The flowers disappeared; the grass and plants were cut short; the marmot and other animals could not find vegetation enough to supply them during the long winter and starved; the mazamas [mountain goats] were killed off; desolation and destruction everywhere . . ."

Around the turn of the last century, climbers of the Mount Adams' south side located their base camps in the western Bird Creek Meadows, which sheepmen still called Happy Valley. A large party of Mazamas, as members of the Portland climbing club were called, were not happy in 1902 when they camped in a meadow transformed by grazing sheep. After the outing, Professor William D. Lyman wrote in the *Mazama* article:

> This paradise, like ancient Eden, has the tail of a serpent. The serpent in this case is the sheep business. The sharp hoofs of the sheep have cut out the turf, defiled the flowery margins of the pools, and polluted the clearness of the fountains. As a result of this, Bird Creek Park has in some places become almost a desert.

A few Native foot trails existed on the lower slopes of Mount Adams for thousands of years, but Indian horse trails dating from the early eighteenth century created an extensive network on all sides of the mountain, giving sheepherders easy access to the higher meadows. Many of those trails were mapped on 1904 and 1926 United States Geological Survey (USGS) 30-minute quadrangles, *"Mount Adams, Wash."* and *"Steamboat Mtn, Wash."* The two historic maps have been out of print since the early 1970s.

For more than six decades, Glenwood horseman and retired forester Leonard Rolph rode horseback on many of the old Native and sheepherder routes before they became completely obscured. For several rainy days in the fall of 2016, Rolph, then eighty-eight, sketched sheep camp names, locations, and trails on a map that I provided. It's invaluable historic information that could not be obtained from any known literature, nor from anyone else alive.

My research has turned up only precious bits of information about sheepherding life on Mount Adams. In the mid-1960s, my father Les Lloyd transcribed his interview

Sheep occupy Hellroaring Meadow in 1922. By the turn of the twentieth century, bands of sheep as large as ten thousand animals were driven to Mount Adams. (U.S. Forest Service)

with an old Glenwood friend and sheepherder, Lloyd Hickey, who first worked as a packer (camp tender) in 1912. Hickey said the Forest Service allowed eleven hundred ewes to a band. A herder and a packer were with each band, and the packer usually had one riding horse and four or five packhorses. Salt blocks had to be carried, along with food supplies for men and sheep dogs. Dog food "was unknown," Hickey said, "and the dogs ate the same as the men." About forty bands of sheep and eighteen hundred head of cows spent winters in Camas Prairie, near the thriving town of Glenwood.

I learned from Herman Kuhnhausen's family book that the packer's duties included finding campsites and bedding grounds for the sheep, as well as making camp, cooking meals, and hunting for lost sheep. Trips to Glenwood for supplies, with packhorses in tow, often would take two or more days. Occasionally a packer would herd the sheep

for a couple of days, so the herder could go to town for supplies. I found no accounts of sheep wagons being used, probably because of the rough country that herders had to traverse. Also, there's no mention of Basque sheepherders, who were so numerous elsewhere in the mountainous West from the late 1800s into the early 1920s.

As kids growing up in the Glenwood Valley during the late 1940s and early '50s, Darvel and I learned about "dough gods"—a form of fried bread—from sheepherder friends of our parents. Horace White, one old-timer who sticks in my mind, cooked them for us over a campfire. A staple in the sheepherder diet on the mountain, dough gods were mixed in the top of a fifty-pound sack of flour. The recipe went something like this: Place an iron frying pan with strips of bacon on a bed of coals. While the bacon is frying, open the sack of flour and use your hands to carve a bowl-shaped depression in the top. Mix a teaspoon or two of baking powder and a little salt with some water in the depression. Surface tension will keep the water from soaking into the flour. Carve in some flour from the sides of the depression, and add more water. Mix to make enough batter for a frying-pan-size dough god no more than an inch thick. Take the bacon out of the frying pan, but leave the grease. Spread the batter in the pan, and make a hole in the middle (about an inch in diameter). Cook it until brown and then flip it over. Cook the other side for a few minutes, then take the dough god out of the pan and stand it up against a stick facing the fire, where it will bake more slowly. Turn it occasionally, and when done, eat with bacon and coffee.

Most of the old sheep camps, such as Island Spring Camp, have since been overgrown by trees and covered with duff. But a careful search can sometimes reveal remains such as rock hearths, cast-iron stove parts and large nails (for hanging things) in old trees closest to the hearths. Other artifacts and evidence may also be visible, but they should not be picked up or disturbed. Cheryl Mack, a retired archaeologist from Trout Lake, warned that it's a violation of federal law to collect artifacts, even cowboy relics, from archaeological and historical sites on federal and tribal lands.

Old sheep camps on the west side of the mountain—some still evident—carry their old names: Divide Camp, Graveyard Camp, Riley Camp, and Lake Camp (different from the "Lake Camp" near Bench Lake). Graveyard Camp was near the 5,440-foot junction of the Stagman Ridge Trail and the old Round-the-Mountain Trail. Several hundred sheep were killed at that spot during a severe storm of unknown date. As to shepherd cabins, very few were constructed on Mount Adams. Still, the remains of one old log cabin can still be found in a meadow about halfway up the Killen Creek Trail on the mountain's northwest side.

Sheepherders named geographical features on all sides of Mount Adams, including Klickitat Glacier, Big Muddy (Creek), Hellroaring Creek (originally "Hell-Roaring"), Little Muddy Creek, The Island, Snowplow Mountain, Smith Butte, Bunnell Butte, King Mountain, McDonald Ridge, Morrison Creek, Crofton Ridge, Salt Creek, Madcat Meadow, Stagman Ridge, Grassy Hill, The Hump, The Bumper, White Salmon Glacier, Burnt Rock, Riley Creek, Mutton Creek, Killen Creek, and Gotchen Creek. The

name Gotchen (pronounced "Gawchun") came from the Goetjen family of Grass Valley, Oregon, who grazed sheep in the area beginning in 1887.

Sled Camp, in a heavily wooded flat on the mountain's west side, was the site of an early trapper's cabin in the late 1800s to early 1900s, said archaeologist Cheryl Mack. A leaning wooden outhouse and cast-iron stove parts are almost all that's left of the camp today.

"These were winter cabins," Mack said, "and the trappers, usually homesteaders from Trout Lake Valley, would use a horse to haul a sled up there in the fall with their supplies. The sled remained abandoned at this site for many years."

Range wars developed when cattle were brought in to graze the southern slopes during the 1890s. Cattlemen coveted the same spring and summer range as the sheep men. The nastiest feuds were in the Glenwood area. Many of the settlers raised cattle and considered the endless bands of sheep travelling through the valley as invaders. No lives were lost in the two decades of conflict, as described in *Early Klickitat Valley Days*, but a number of sheepherders and camp tenders were injured in shootings and their camp outfits destroyed. Several herders were almost lynched one night by more than fifty men with flour-sack hoods over their heads. Meanwhile, Glenwood grew into a rip-roaring western town by the turn of the century, and businesses thrived thanks to the massive sheep drives.

Tensions on the range eased somewhat after Mount Adams was included in the new Columbia National Forest in 1908. Ranger districts were established a year later and the mountain divided into grazing allotments, most of them designated for sheep. Grazing regulations, such as permits and fees, were implemented for conservation of grazing lands; though decades would pass before conservation was achieved.

To enforce the new regulations, the Forest Service built the Gotchen Creek Ranger Station in 1909. Costing $332 to build, the two-room cabin was strategically located in a meadow at 3,700 feet on the south side of the mountain. Nearly all bands of sheep heading to Mount Adams Ranger District allotments, from the southeast side clockwise to the north side, would pass by the new station on a wagon road originating in Glenwood. Forest Ranger

A shepherd leads his flock into the Glenwood Valley from the lower flanks of Adams in 1971.

Homer Ross was somehow able to count and record the many thousands of sheep each season; those counts are now historical record. Ross's home in Glenwood doubled as the Mount Adams Ranger District headquarters, but the Gotchen Creek cabin served as the summer headquarters of the Ranger District until 1917.

Even with new Forest Service regulations and modest limits of grazing activity, significant resource damage continued on Mount Adams. Long ago I remember Ernie Childs of Trout Lake telling stories about the "damned sheep." Childs was an old-time cattleman and Forest Service employee back then. In a taped interview, Childs recounted that between 1912 and 1918 the flanks of Mount Adams were so badly overrun with sheep that "clouds of dust" were created whenever the sheep were moved. According to a sheep spokesman in 1919, during the summer, some 1.3 million sheep were grazing on federal "forest reserves" in Oregon and Washington.

Also around 1919 the Forest Service set aside a portion of Bird Creek Meadows (five hundred acres) as a public recreation area. By 1926 sheep numbers on Mount Adams were still huge, in the order of seventy-five thousand. However, this was about a 50 percent reduction from a quarter-century earlier. Ernie Childs told how into the early 1930s, cattlemen complained to the Forest Service that sheep were "tromping the country to pieces." At the same time, cattle numbered about fifteen hundred head.

It was high time for a change, and in 1933 the new district ranger, K. C. Langfield, was finally the man to do it. Childs remembered Langfield as a "stickler," who "regularly inspected sheep camps and sheep allotments and made the sheepherders move their camp and bed grounds every night." Ranger Langfield converted some areas from sheep to cattle range. He served as district ranger until 1956, becoming a legendary character and also a friend of my parents.

Other factors contributed to gradually diminishing sheep numbers during the 1930s and '40s. Fire suppression by the Forest Service led to less forage as young trees filled in grassy meadows. After World War II, Americans' appetite for mutton and lamb fell dramatically, and numbers of sheep raised followed suit. The sheep range in the Bird Creek allotment (south of Bird Creek Meadows) was finally closed in 1962. My brother Darvel and I encountered perhaps the last large band of sheep on the mountain in 1970. The sheep were in Glacier Basin at timberline on

Sheep grazed Muddy Meadows, at the northern base of the mountain, for at least seven decades.

the northwest side. I'll never forget the all-pervading odor, and what little was left of the trampled and chewed tundra vegetation. We chatted with the lonely, last sheepherder while trying not to show our dismay.

Ecosystem management wasn't a Forest Service priority until the onset of "new forestry" practices in the 1990s. Information on the ecological impacts of sheep grazing on Mount Adams seemed more anecdotal than scientific. We have Wilhelm Suksdorf's early testimony about animals such as mountain goats being totally decimated. Based on my own observations and research, mountain goats disappeared for at least seventy years following

the advent of sheep grazing. The first goats that we saw on Mount Adams were in the mid-1970s. Their strong recovery began in the 1980s, thanks to migration from Goat Rocks, mountain goat management by the Yakama Nation, and minimal hunting pressure. Elk are also back in large numbers.

Forest Service personnel used the former Gotchen Creek Ranger Station into the 1990s, and it has been restored. It's the oldest building in Gifford Pinchot National Forest and the only permanent cabin on Mount Adams. Still ahead: approval for the Forest Service plan to include the historic cabin in the public rental system.

Chapter 4

The Era of C. E. Rusk

For more than ten thousand feet the superb mountain towered above the valley, with no intervening heights to mar the view, and the effect was one of indescribable grandeur.

— C. E. Rusk

Claude Ewing Rusk—known as C. E.—was the first non-Indian to explore the many faces of Mount Adams. He became a legend in his own time, especially after the 1924 publication of his classic book, *Tales of a Western Mountaineer*. The book spans nearly a half century and much of it is devoted to Mount Adams. Rusk's loyalty to the mountain, and the love story he wrote about it, is perhaps unmatched in mountaineering literature.

As young boys, Darvel and I were captivated by Rusk's *Tales*, and to a certain extent we followed in his footsteps (and horse tracks). When Mountaineers Books chose to print a second edition of Rusk's book in 1978, I wrote a detailed biography of the author as a lengthy introduction, including previously unpublished photos that I'd uncovered in my research.

A decade or so before young Rusk entered the scene, Euro-American settlers began homesteading at the base of Mount Adams in Camas Prairie. Two German families, the Trohs and Wellenbrocks, established farms in the valley in 1878. In the summer of 1882, Henry F. Troh had a somber reason to ride his horse to the 5,700-foot bluff top above Mirror Lake. Mourning the deaths of three of his five children to diphtheria, he dismounted and found a spot where he could see both his farm in the valley far below and the southeast face of Mount Adams high above. On a bedrock outcrop of glassy, black dacite lava, Henry chiseled his initials and date, "HFT 1882." A century later in the early 1990s, I discovered the inscription and notified the Troh family and Yakama Nation. It may be the oldest evidence of Euro-American presence on the mountain. Unfortunately, the intense heat of the 2015 Cougar Creek Fire caused part of the inscription to spall off.

Claude Rusk was only two in 1874 when his family moved to the Columbia Hills of Klickitat County. Until his mid-teens, he could only fantasize about the "great white mountain" on the horizon. Writing in his 1924 book, Rusk remembered how, as a sixteen-year-old in 1888, he finally rode horseback with his parents to within three miles of the "stupendous precipices and tortured icefalls" of Mount Adams' east face. The following year at seventeen, he began teaching at a "little log schoolhouse" at the southern edge of Camas Prairie, and that same year, climbed Mount Adams for the first time with his uncle Maxwell. Rusk boarded at the pioneer home of Jane Myers (who lived near the schoolhouse), and he was enthralled by the grandeur of the mountain rising two miles above the valley.

In September 1890, Rusk wrote, he circumnavigated Mount Adams with his mother Josie and twelve-year-old sister Leah. It was a horseback journey counter-clockwise around the mountain, and with their "hack" (horse-drawn carriage or wagon), the three started riding north on "rough, roundabout roads" from the Rusk family's Klickitat River homestead. On the second day they left their hack along the upper Klickitat Canyon, crossed the Big Muddy on a "shaky sheep-bridge" and continued over to the mountain's eastern flank. Having lost the trail, another day of slow progress took them to a vale on the north side of Sheepherders' Butte (later named Goat Butte). Wet snow during the night and no tent made it

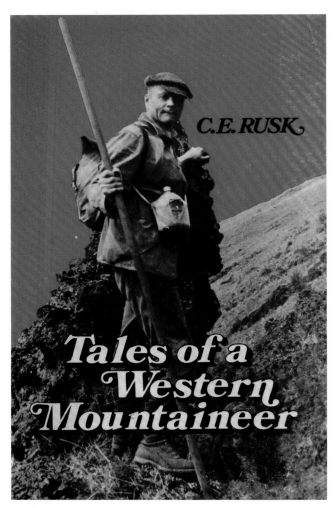

My "Portrait of C. E. Rusk" introduced readers to the author in the 1978 rerelease of *Tales* by Mountaineers Books. (Courtesy Mountaineers Books)

debris-covered snout of Klickitat Glacier, "a scene of grand desolation." It was the source of the Big Muddy, the largest stream on Mount Adams.

The next day they climbed above timberline and set foot on what was later called "Rusk Glacier." They continued with a sick horse below the terminus of the Wilson Glacier and into the Muddy Fork lava flow below Red Butte on the north. While descending into more friendly terrain, two sheepherders with their bands of sheep told them where to find Indian encampments. In *Tales of a Western Mountaineer*, Rusk remembered how their party surprised a "small cavalcade" of Indians on the trail. One spoke perfect English and appeared to be well-educated. Rusk described the camps as picturesque scenes of animation and bright colors. He said the women devoted their time to picking and drying huckleberries, while the men hunted, horse-raced, and gambled.

Re-ascending and continuing westward on their 1890 journey around the mountain, the Rusks had trouble following this upper trail. It was an Indian trail, but infrequently used because the main Indian routes on the northwest side had traversed lower on the mountain toward the huckleberry fields. The Rusks would let their horses graze while scouting for the trail. While his mother and sister waited, young Claude rambled higher to a moraine, where he discovered glistening ice at the base of a great glacier. It was Adams Glacier, the largest on the mountain.

Their next camp was in the subalpine parkland belt on the western side, where they had an excellent view of the west face dominated by The Pinnacle, the 12,000-foot-high west summit. Rusk wrote that it was "probably the least interesting side of the great peak," but worth visiting because of its "three considerable glaciers, a remarkable icefall, and fine precipices." Continuing their circuit and after crossing their last jagged lava flow on the south side, he wrote, they entered the "wonderful Bird Creek Meadows" and found the trail that "bore down the long slope to Camas Prairie." They still had a long ride to retrieve their hack.

Rusk wrote that two "firsts" were accomplished by their historic circumnavigation. Josie and Leah were the first "white womankind" to make the complete circuit of the mountain. Claude also claimed to be the first person

a gloomy morning, prompting them to explore the area and wait out the weather. It was a serendipitous decision. They rode to the top of 7,500-foot Goat Butte when the skies cleared. Years later, he recalled an "awe-compelling majesty of the east side" revealed itself. A thousand feet below lay "the Elysian land, a veritable mountain paradise," where they knew they must camp.

The stillness of the night was broken by what he called a "wild, shrieking roar." A massive ice avalanche a vertical mile above their camp came thundering down the 2,000-foot headwall onto the glacier. When morning arrived, Avalanche Valley had its name. Leaving their horses to enjoy the grassy meadow, the Rusk party continued to explore. They hiked across rugged terrain to view the

to see all of the mountain's glaciers "and to know them as glaciers." As a teenager and a new teacher, Rusk had entered the realm of real exploration and discovery, and it seems that henceforth he preferred to be called "C. E."

In 1894 a small group of self-proclaimed "real mountain climbers" from Portland founded the Mazamas (the Spanish word for mountain goat). The first climbing club in the Pacific Northwest was formally organized on top of Mount Hood during a summer sleet storm; although out of one hundred ninety-three men and women who reached the summit of Hood on that day, only forty or so stayed to vote. This was a historic occasion for the sport of mountaineering, and it set in motion the club's ongoing activities of annual climbs and outings in the Cascades.

The summit of Mount Adams in July 1895 was the second formal climb of the Mazamas. Rusk was living next to the Klickitat River at the time and, with a friend named M. F. Derting, rode horses to the mountain intending to join the group. Climbing much faster, they easily passed the Portlanders and were first to the summit. But later in the day, about twenty-five members of the Mazamas

Top: C. E. Rusk described this vista of Klickitat Glacier, photographed in 1895 from the Ridge of Wonders crest, as "one of earth's sublimest viewpoints." (William D. Lyman; Darryl Lloyd Collection) *Above:* Henry F. Troh, one of the earliest pioneers in the Glenwood Valley, chiseled his initials in bedrock dacite lava near Bluff Lake in 1882.

reached the summit—nearly as many as the entire number of people who had climbed the mountain prior to 1895. One Mazamas member, Professor Edgar McClure of the University of Oregon, used an aneroid barometer, mercurial barometer, and boiling point thermometer to

On a reconnaissance of the Wilson Glacier icefall in 1919, C. E. Rusk cuts steps with only a hatchet. (J. Howard Green; Darryl Lloyd Collection)

determine the mountain's elevation at between 12,150 and 12,402 feet. On that same historic day, Mazamas climbing parties were scaling other major Northwest peaks, such as Mounts Rainier, Hood, and Jefferson. The climbers carried various kinds of signaling equipment—heliograph mirrors, kits, and carrier pigeons. The intent was to exchange messages and communicate with their Portland base. Smoke from major forest fires foiled their effort, although some signals were exchanged between Adams and Hood. It was the beginning of the Mazamas' long history of scientific investigations in the Cascades.

Later in 1895 a Mazamas party visited three glaciers: White Salmon (Avalanche Glacier included), Mazama, and Klickitat. Professor W. D. Lyman colorfully described

them a year later in "The Glaciers of Mount Adams," in the first *Mazama* publication. The published photo was a dramatic shot of Klickitat Glacier from the crest of Ridge of Wonders. Lyman wrote: "The savage grandeur and the overwhelming immensity of this glacier beggar the power of the pen to describe."

C. E. Rusk, who named Ridge of Wonders, hiked to the same location a month or so after Lyman. In *Tales of a Western Mountaineer*, Rusk called it "one of earth's sublimest viewpoints," and he went on to described it in colorful words: "The three-thousand-foot eastern precipice was close at hand. From the summit icecap, between the richly colored cliffs, to the fearful chaos of the glacier's upper end, the tumultuous ice-falls bore their burden of massed and broken blocks. Here was the home of avalanche and storm."

With Rusk's invaluable assistance, in August 1901 Professor Harry F. Reid undertook the first systematic study and mapping of the Mount Adams glaciers. A well-known glaciologist from Johns Hopkins University, Reid had come west earlier in July to study the glaciers of Mount Hood. He selected Rusk to be his personal guide and packer for several weeks of fieldwork. Their complete circuit of the mountain by horseback, foot, and two pack-horses is richly described in *Tales*. Rusk makes lighthearted fun of their three-meal daily diet consisting of nothing but coffee, fried bread (likely a version of dough gods), and bacon. Diverting by foot to seventeen viewpoint "stations" along the way, Reid photographed, mapped with a plane table, and named all ten principal glaciers. An infected foot injury rendered him unable to walk at the journey's end. Reid's study was documented in the 1905 *Mazama*, published locally, and the 1906 *Annuals of Glaciology*, published in Germany. "Mount Adams would no longer be an unrecorded peak," wrote Rusk. Today, Reid's glacier photographs are used as the standard for baseline comparisons of rapid glacial retreat on Mount Adams and Mount Hood.

The 1904 USGS *Mount Adams, Wash.* quadrangle was the first topographic map of the area. Fieldwork for the 1904 map was conducted by topographer A. H. Sylvester and one assistant. The topographers surveyed the eight-hundred-twenty-eight-square-mile area on horseback during 1903 and 1904. Sylvester plotted the topography

Top: Rusk, far right, poses with his Cascadians party in 1921 prior to their first ascent of the east face. (Top: Maurice H. Barnes; Darryl Lloyd Collection) *Above:* A 2011 photo of the same spot; note the growth of the four subalpine firs.

in the field, using a plane table equipped with a telescopic alidade for vertical-angle arcs. I believe these unheralded men are among the most important non-Native explorers of Mount Adams country.

The 1904 USGS map is also amazingly accurate. My brother Darvel and I used it with the 1926 30-minute quadrangle (taped together) for navigation until the new 7.5-minute USGS quads were published in the early 1970s. I also used the 1904/1926 maps to make a scale model of Mount Adams for a University of Colorado cartography class in 1968.

The Mountaineers were formed in Seattle in 1906. Five years later in 1911, a party of sixty-nine hearty members of the club made a remarkable one-hundred-sixty-two-mile, twenty-one-day trek down the crest of the South Cascades from Mount Rainier to the Columbia River. Along the way, fifty-four of them traversed Mount Adams over the summit from north to south, starting from "Killing Creek" (Killen Creek). The entire journey required sixteen different camps and thirty pack horses from Glenwood for support. A photo of the group heading for the base of the North Cleaver appears in the wonderful book *The Guardians of the Columbia*, published in 1912 by John H. Williams.

Williams' book publicized the three "guardian" volcanoes—Mounts Hood, Adams, and St. Helens—with its many turn-of-the-century photos and colorful prose. It certainly qualifies as the best, if not the first, guidebook on the three mountains at that time. Included are notes about transportation routes, mountain clubs, guides, and hotels. About Mount Adams, Williams wrote: "During the present summer, a hotel is to be erected a short distance from the end of Mazama Glacier, at an altitude of about sixty-five hundred feet, overlooking Hellroaring Canyon on one side, and on the other a delightful region of mountain tarns, waterfalls and alpine flower meadows [Bird Creek Meadows]." Back then only horse trails led to the mountain from Trout Lake and Glenwood; it would be decades before the Bird Creek Road was built. Seems that Williams' vision of a hotel in Bird Creek Meadows was wishful thinking.

While large groups climbed the two easier routes on the north and south sides of Mount Adams, C. E. Rusk had long dreamed of making a first ascent of the east face, which was by far the steepest face on the mountain. In 1919,

Rusk explored high on the east face with only an alpenstock and hatchet, wanting to scout a feasible route to the summit. It was shortly after the end of World War I and prominent features lacked names at the time. Rusk named Wilson Glacier after Woodrow Wilson, and the sharp red ridge between Wilson and Rusk glaciers, he named Victory Ridge. Rusk was the first to climb high on Victory Ridge, on Wilson Glacier (with a companion), and on Lava Ridge of the northeast face.

On Victory Ridge, Rusk spent a night huddled alone on the highest place he could safely reach. He called it "Camp of the Stars" and took photos of the headwalls for future reference. Directly to the north of his bivouac site is a prominent crag in the middle of Wilson Glacier. Rusk named the crag Roosevelt Cliff after President Theodore Roosevelt. Afterwards, the Roosevelt Cliff name stuck to a wall of more impressive cliffs that are much higher on the face.

In the decade preceding the 1924 publication of his *Tales of a Western Mountaineer*, C. E. Rusk was among very few vocal conservationists in the Northwest. He was a great admirer of Teddy Roosevelt, and he appealed for the preservation of the mountain he loved most. Rusk felt it was high time for the "so long neglected" Mount Adams "to be accorded the recognition it deserves." He was distressed by the torching of subalpine firs for sport and the ravaging of high meadows by sheep, which, like John Muir, he called "hoofed locusts." Rusk joined a city of Yakima citizens' campaign in 1919 to set aside most of the mountain as a national park. The name they chose was "Yakima National Park." To promote the park, Rusk wrote a twenty-six-page booklet titled, *Mount Adams: Towering Sentinel of the Lower Columbia—Reasons for Its Preservation and Maintenance as a National Park*. The proposal drew vigorous opposition from cattle, sheep, and Grange associations in Klickitat County. As a result, the effort failed in Congress without a vote.

C. E. Rusk was said to have "no superior as a mountaineer," having lived and climbed in the North Cascades the previous decade and, in 1910, making a valiant attempt to summit Mount McKinley (now called Denali).

In the summer of 1921, while living in Yakima, Rusk said the time had come to "accept the challenge" of the perilous east face of Mount Adams. As founding

The Cascadians' route ascended Rusk Glacier (lower center), then directly up the middle of The Castle (left center), where the team survived a long night before continuing to the summit.

president of The Cascadians club, he organized a group of twenty members (including a fourteen-year old girl) for an eleven-day outing to the east side. It took a day by car and two days by pack train to cross the Yakama Reservation and reach their base camp at 6,500 feet in Avalanche Valley. Their route took them by Mount Adams Lake, the largest lake on the mountain.

After a number of days of exploring in the area, Rusk chose six of the strongest climbers for the east face summit climb: W. E. Richardson, Clarence Starcher, Clarence Truitt, Robert E. Williams, Rolland Whitmore, and Edgar Coursen. At three-thirty in the morning of August 14, 1921, the hardy group set off on their epic "Conquest of the Great East Side." According to the late climbing legend Fred Becky, Rusk's "was an outstanding achievement in courage."

The thirty-nine-hour saga is related in thrilling detail in *Tales of a Western Mountaineer*. The men wore hobnailed boots; Rusk and Richardson had Swiss ice axes, and the other five had steel-pointed alpenstocks. They all tied into a hundred-foot rope and zigzagged up the steep and "badly crevassed" Rusk Glacier, stopping frequently to cut steps in the hard ice. After reaching the great bergschrund

at the foot of a prominent castle-like feature called The Castle, the climb got serious. Rusk wrote: "There was a danger that no skill could avoid, a peril that must be met by the mountaineer if he would accomplish things worthwhile in mountaineering." The next 1,500 feet took most of the day (as well as eight pages of *Tales*). The most difficult and dangerous part was scaling a series of vertical loose-rock chimneys.

After building a cairn on the flat 11,400-foot crest of The Castle and with only four hours of daylight left, Rusk noticed storm clouds approaching. Instead of risking a 900-foot climb to the summit in a whiteout, through a minefield of deep crevasses and seracs, Rusk decided to bivouac. None of the climbers had extra clothing, food, or shelter. Snow and hail pelted them throughout their fifteen-hour ordeal. At night the thundering roar of ice avalanches from overhanging ice cliffs nearby made their "blood run cold." When shivering could no longer be tolerated, all but one of the men walked back and forth to restore circulation, over and over again to the point of exhaustion. Morning broke at last, and the rising sun was clear to the east. The smell of sulfur gasses emitting from nearby crevasses was in the air. When clouds closed

On top of The Castle at 11,400 feet, Darvel signs the climbers' register in 1976. Also on the rock cairn are a commemorative plaque and an urn containing C. E. Rusk's ashes.

in once again, they used a pocket compass and carefully worked their way around enormous crevasses to reach the summit around noon. It was now more than thirty-two hours after leaving Avalanche Valley, and they still had to negotiate the long descent and difficult traverse back to camp by way of Mazama and Klickitat glaciers.

When they finally trooped into camp, Rusk hadn't eaten for thirty-nine hours. His team had accomplished a feat that many thought was impossible. In the history of Pacific Northwest mountaineering, his bold east face ascent was probably the most significant climb of the era.

In 1923 Rusk moved from Yakima to Grants Pass, Oregon. He continued to climb and adventure in the wilds. In 1931, only months after a near-disastrous experience near Mount St. Elias in Canada, he died of heart disease at fifty-nine. Complying with his last request, Rusk's old Cascadian friends placed his ashes at the top of The Castle in a brass urn. They mortared it in place

on a large rock cairn in the middle of the 300-foot-wide flat, and they also left an inscribed plaque.

In 1976, during a climb of the east face of Mount Adams by the north Klickitat Icefall route, Darvel and I made a short diversion over to its crest. The urn containing Rusk's ashes was missing from the rock cairn. After a quick search, we found it very close to tumbling down onto Rusk Glacier, a thousand feet below. The dark surface of the urn looked burned, so it probably was struck by lightning. We carried the heavy urn back and restored it to the cairn, placing it next to a plaque inscribed: "C. E. RUSK 10 ORE." and "SONS OF UNION VETERANS" and a climbers' register. After signing the register, Darvel and I continued climbing directly up the steep headwall to Mount Adams' summit—a first ascent of the headwall. A friend reported the plaque and urn were still there in 1995. I would love to know if Rusk's ashes still rest in that awesome setting today.

Chapter 5

The Summit Lookout

I am . . . an extremist, one who lives and loves by choice far out on the very verge of things,
on the edge of the abyss, where this world falls off into the depths of another.

— Edward Abbey

Fire detection and suppression became the highest priority of the U.S. Forest Service after 1910, following a devastating wildfire in Idaho and Montana that burned three million acres and killed eighty-seven people. The Forest Service began building fire lookouts in national forests across the country. The first lookout on top of a high Cascade strato-volcano was on Mount Lassen in northern California in 1913, although less than a year later, it was destroyed in an explosive eruption. The second was built on Mount Hood in 1915. Next came lookouts on the summits of Mount St. Helens and Mount Adams; both projects began in 1918 and were completed in 1921.

At the time, the Mount Adams fire lookout was second highest in the United States behind 13,214-foot Fairview Peak Lookout in Colorado, built around 1912. But the Mount Adams building would be perhaps the most difficult to construct in the country.

Several tons of lumber and materials were trucked to the end of the road at Morrison Creek Camp on the south side of the mountain. The staging area was about eight miles from the summit. It took the rest of the summer of 1918 for packer Dan Lewis of Randle, Washington, to transport the materials to a flat area at 7,400 feet below The Crescent (later named Crescent Glacier).

In 1919, Art Jones, Adolph Schmid, Julius "Jude" Wang, and Jessie Robbins were hired to get the materials to the summit. It was a three-mile trudge and vertical elevation gain of almost 5,000 feet. Photos show that certain materials like windows and two-by-eight beams were carried on their backs. Art Jones took the heaviest loads, normally ninety pounds at a time. The men camped on the summit

in two tents fastened end-to-end, against a low rock wall to help break the wind. Even so, tents were lost in storms several times while left unattended.

Jones devised an ingenious system using sleds to transport other materials up the snow-covered slopes of Suksdorf Ridge. A triangular frame with a large pulley wheel was anchored a few hundred feet upslope. Telephone wire ran through the pulley with one end secured to the bottom sled that held the building materials. The other end was attached to a second sled filled with canvas bags of wet snow, and then positioned near the pulley at the top. The sacks of heavy snow in the upper sled served as counterweights and could be jettisoned if the payload sled got out of control. A set of empty sacks accompanied the loaded sled, to be filled with snow for the next run. This procedure worked well and was repeated many times. By the end of the 1919 summer season, all materials had reached the summit of Mount Adams.

Actual construction began in early summer of 1920, with Jones and Schmid doing most of the work. Other men helped for brief periods. Photos by Jones show a partially framed building surrounded by deep snow. Cables attached to buried rocks anchored the corners of the building. Through storm and fury, the lookout was finally completed in the summer of 1921. Similar to the design of the lookouts on Mounts Hood and St. Helens, it had a fourteen-by-fourteen-foot first floor and six-by-six-foot cupola with windows on all sides.

During construction, the two men had the additional duty to spot and report fires, using a phone located in one of the tents. Two phone wires ran from the base of the

In 1919 and 1920, several tons of lumber and materials had to be humanly hauled to the summit from the 7,400-foot level. Art Jones normally carried ninety pounds at a time. (Ardith Thompson Collection)

mountain to the summit. The end of the ground wire was placed in Morrison Creek below The Crescent, and poles suspended the live wire to keep it from contacting snow or rock. Maintenance of the suspended wire proved impossible after wind and ice storms. However, the men discovered that the phone worked fine with both wires lying on the mountain's surface, even when the live wire was buried under the winter snowpack.

Jones and Schmid manned the lookout during the 1921 and 1922 seasons and their physical efforts during this time were amazing. At the start of each season, they carried to the summit about eighteen hundred pounds of supplies on their backs. One morning while hauling up supplies, they spotted a fire near the base of the mountain. After hurrying to the top, they found the phone not functioning, so they raced back down thousands of feet, fixed the break in the wire and returned to the summit to report the blaze. Then after watching the fire flare up with no one fighting it, Jones and Schmid zoomed down the mountain again—this time in makeshift sleds and with shovels. The two quickly romped over to the blaze, dug a line around it, and then assisted the Forest Service firefighters when they finally arrived.

Chaffin Johnson, who took over Schmid's lookout job in 1923, told this story about Art Jones:

> I was 22 years old and Art was strong as a horse. I would carry about 65 pounds and Art would take 90 pounds. One day I decided to show off, so I strapped a case of kerosene, which weighed about 100 pounds, to my pack. Art put on a case of kerosene, then added a case of milk, a total of 150 pounds. We both made it to the lookout without stopping, but the next trip I selected 65 pounds and Art 90 pounds.

I met with Art Jones' daughter, Ardith Thompson, in 2012 in Trout Lake, where she and her husband lived. Ardith graciously allowed me to reproduce a selection of prints from her father's photo album. As I was photographing the album on her dining room table, she told me more about Jones's routine during the summer of 1922.

Every other weekend, Jones would walk the nineteen miles from the top of Mount Adams to his home on Jennings Road in Trout Lake. He would go to church, have dinner with his father, and the next day return to his job at the second-highest Forest Service lookout in

Left: A flag flies on the new U.S. Forest Service lookout building in 1922. Between 1913 and 1921, similar lookouts were built on Mounts Lassen, Hood, and St. Helens. (Ardith Thompson Collection) *Right:* Standing on The Pinnacle, Art Jones was in charge of the lookout, visible in the upper left corner, from 1921 through 1923. (Ardith Thompson Collection)

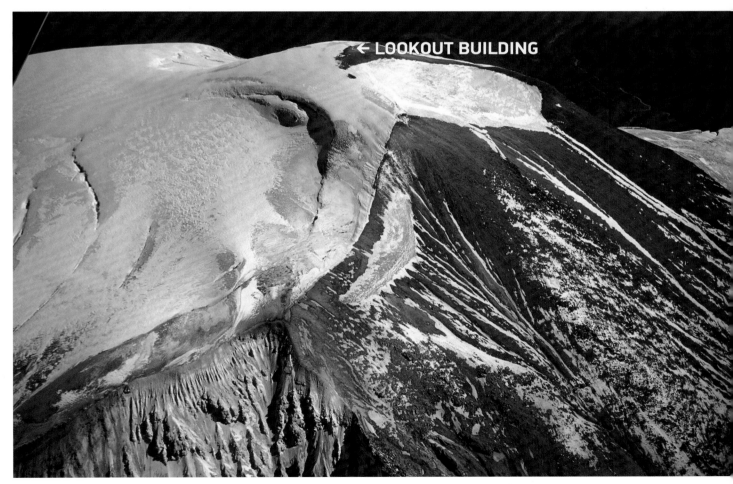

← LOOKOUT BUILDING

The summit cone and remains of the lookout building are shown in this aerial photo, taken from the southwest.

the country. Jones's commute took him three and a half hours to reach timberline and another three and a half hours to climb the mountain, a total of seven hours to gain almost 10,400 feet over the nineteen-mile distance. His backpack was undoubtedly full on each of those many trips to the summit.

Years later, Jones related how he and Schmid cut the bottoms out of kerosene cans and then fashioned them into a crude toboggan. Sledding, it would take only about twenty minutes to get down the mountain, said his daughter Ardith.

The summer of 1923 was Art Jones' last season as fire lookout. He and Chaffin Johnson well documented the season in separate accounts. Jones kept a small notebook while he was on lookout duty. Fortunately the notebook exists in Ardith Thompson's collection, and I was able to copy some of the more interesting notations. They begin on July 12, 1923, and are transcribed as Jones wrote them. A few notes of my own appear in italics.

12 Electric storm in evening. Got a light shock by holding my knife blade up.

14 Very stormy day. Hail, snow and rain. Electric storm at 12:30. Saw lightning strike in green timber in vicinity of Little Goose Creek near Sunrise Trail. . . . hard to distinguish between smoke and fog.

15 Run ½ mile of new wire from first summit and repaired rest of old line to lookout. Heavy wind all night and day. Clouds blowing over lookout . . .

21 Heavy haze and smoke almost obscure vision. Smoke level about 12,000 ft.

24 Got call from office about 1:30. Bird Creek fire under control. Good view in evening. Diamond Peak, Three Sisters, Jefferson, Hood, Helens, Rainier, Baker plainly visible from lookout.

25 Went down and got 10 gal oil in evening.

26 Phone in good condition.

27 Very warm quiet night. Smokey in every direction. Heavy smoke coming from west. Call from office concerning flag for lookout.

29 Good view. Light breezes blowing from Northwest. Sulphur fumes very strong. Five visitors arrive at

9 AM. Went down in afternoon to Guler after new stove, telephone wire and oil.
Guler was the original town center, one mile from the present Trout Lake market.

30 Music over phone from Chain of Lakes.
Jones reported all calls, business and social. He noted many evenings with "music from Chain Lakes." I'm wondering, was the lookout station at Chain of Lakes staffed by a single woman trying to woo Art?

31 Left Morrison at 6 AM. Warm quiet cloudy smoky day. Very poor vision. Took new stove where pack string stopped (*below Crescent Glacier*) and packed to lookout. Music from Chain Lakes over phone in evening.

August 1 Went over to first summit and took up old emergency wire.

2 . . . went down and got pack of oil at top of Crescent.

3 Heavy clouds around Lookout, unable to see in any direction.

6 9 AM went down and brought pack to Lookout.

7 Went down and brought up pack in afternoon.

8 Built fire finder table and set finder up.

9 Called Little Huckleberry at 9 AM for mirror flashes to help align the fire finder. Good success. Called Red Mt. 9:40 AM for mirror flash for check line. Check Reading correct.

Went down and took pictures on east side of Middle Summit.

Call from Morrison Creek 7 PM Mountain climber.

10 Very cold night up in my BVDs impractical joke. Sighted fire in Columbia National Forest near Hemlock. Reported to Guler Station.

11 Very smoky in every direction very dim views. Heavy wind from South. Social call office 10:30 AM. Shoveled snow drift SW of Lookout down so view thru fire finder would be unobstructed. Social call Chain Lakes 11:30. Eight large hawks circle top of Mt and fly north. Unable to see flashes from Anvil Rock on Rainier on account of clouds. Call from Osborne 7:30 PM.

A large climbing party on the northwest side was photographed in the early 1920s, presumably by Jones, who manned the lookout at the time. (Ardith Thompson Collection)

Left: Straddling a small crevasse, Chaffin Johnson took over Adolph Schmid's lookout job in 1923. He was Jones's partner for only that season. (Ardith Thompson Collection) *Right:* Art Jones examines hailstones following the frightful lightning storm of August 21, 1923. (Ardith Thompson Collection)

14 Went down and got roll of telephone wire. Started 11:10, back 2PM.

15 Stringing new telephone line from first summit to base of middle summit.

17 Heavy wind all night and very smoky in all directions. Vision very dim.

19 Wind coming from South. Very restricted view. Visitors arrive 12:30 to 2PM. 3 PM Rain and hail. 4 PM heavy clouds and snow . . .

21 started tanning bobcat hide.

4:30 heavy clouds envelope lookout. Strong east and Southwest wind meet on mt. Hail storm 4:30 PM. Hail stones as big as walnuts coming straight down. one glanced and went thru S.W. window. 5:10 Hell broke loose and we had fire works with capital F. One blinding flash after another till about 9 PM. quiet for about 10 minutes. 10 PM Lightning hit tower and went down Southeast anchor cable, jarred door open and wind blew snow all over house. Had to get up in snow storm in bare feet and underwear and nail the door in place. Storm passed about 2:30 AM.

22 Sighted fires on Indian reservation and west of Glenwood. Made out reports but couldn't report on account of telephone being out of order. . . . Found part of line melted on middle summit from lightning. Went back up Lookout and got extra wire and went down and repaired line and went back up and reported fires to H. A. Welty at Guler.

25 Large rock shattered on first summit by lightning. *On the first summit, or Pikers Peak, Jones chiseled this inscription on the boulder: "Lightning struck this rock on Aug. 25, 1923."*

26 Music from Chain Lakes 8 PM till 9:10 PM.

27 Clear morning. warm and heavy sulfur fumes. Northwest breezes blowing.
On this day, Jones chiseled these words on a west-facing boulder at a little over 11,500 feet on the first summit:

> YOU ARE A PIKER IF
> YOU STOP ON THIS SUMMIT.
> DON'T CRAB. THE MOUNTAIN
> WAS HERE FIRST.
> ARTHUR JONES

It became known as Pikers Peak, also called the "false summit." Jones found more breaks in the wire where, he wrote, "lightning burned the line and went into Mt. ground." After repairing the telephone wire, Jones reported numerous fires to the Forest Service.

29 Earthquake 7:40 AM.
Jones's partner Chaffin Johnson had just stepped into the cabin and grabbed a bunk to keep from falling. As Johnson related: "Art shouted from the cupola, 'Stop swinging on the guy cable or you will shake the building off the foundation.' Then he looked down and realized it was an earthquake."

31 Took pack from Morrison Creek to Lookout (supplies).

Sept. 2 Heavy cloud fields forming and water running out of the fog around the lookout - gale blowing from west.

4 Took old oil stove down mt and brought back pack left lookout 9 AM. Arrived lookout with 108 lbs 8:30 PM.

6 Very clear day.
Jones reported many fires in Washington and Oregon on this day.

8 Very smoky in low country, very clear above 9,000 ft. level. Cleaned up all trash and took picture of lookout. Went over to West Summit.

9 Made trail up middle summit.
Found grey squirrel in ice near lookout.

13 Buried rubbish. Cleaned yard and put lower shutters in place.

14 Heavy wind from everywhere. Continuous whirlwinds traveling in every direction. Dust, sand and gravel clouds fill the air. Heavy clouds in west and north. Very cold day.

18 West wind blowing in morning, quite cloudy high up. good view. Called office.

This was the last entry in Art Jones's notebook. It seems odd that there are no entries by Jones about the lookout on the summit of Mount St. Helens. Perhaps no telephone link existed between the two fire lookouts.

On August 27, 1923, Art Jones chiseled this inscription on a large, west-facing boulder, known at the time as the "first summit." It was henceforth called Pikers Peak; the name becoming official in 1974.

Chaffin Johnson expanded on Jones's account of the hail and lightning storm that hit the summit of Mount Adams on August 21, 1923. His story appeared in the *Oregon Journal* newspaper in 1968. Johnson wrote that he knew a bad storm was coming and had told climbers below the first summit to get off the mountain as quickly as possible.

I hurried back up the mountain, but stopped about a mile below the lookout and cut the telephone wire. At the station I cut it again and pulled the wire well away from the building. A few moments later the fireworks started. About every 10 seconds a ball of fire would jump off the end of the wire.

We were in the center of the storm. There was lightning below us and above us and right where we were. It began hailing. The stones were the size of large walnuts. They came straight down and bounced. It appeared that as much hail was going up as was coming down. One stone came in at an angle, bounced and broke a window. When the storm stopped, the hail stones were six inches deep. The storm backed off for awhile; then it started to blow and snow, and the lightning hammered the mountain top again. Finally the storm passed on and we went to bed with the thunder rumbling in the distance.

I woke up to find the lookout tower jumping and the door in bed with Art. Snow was blowing in. I held the door while Art went for hammer and nails. A terrific gust of wind struck the building and blew me and the door over. We wrestled it back in place and nailed it closed. It was then we discovered that the hinges were a mass of melted metal. We later found that lightning had blasted several large rocks near the building. A black glass-like substance had melted and run out of them. "Never again," I told Art. "Amen, brother," he answered.

With Mount Rainier in the background, Pikers Peak (at left) and the summit lookout are clearly visible. Parts of the 1930s horse trail are barely discernible.

Art Jones probably lost track of the number of times he climbed Mount Adams during his five seasons on the mountain, ending in September 1923. If records were kept, he almost certainly would be the champion with hundreds of ascents, most with ninety-pound loads.

The last year that the Mount Adams lookout operated was 1924. Two new men, Rudolph Dietrich and Ernie Cowell, manned the station that season. Because of poor visibility, they were off-duty as much as they were on. Persistent clouds covered the summit on many days, and even on cloudless days, heavy smoke and haze in the atmosphere made it too difficult to spot fires. At the end of the season, the lookout was boarded up indefinitely.

It cost the taxpayers back then $8,000 to build, which is well over $100,000 in today's dollars.

Mount St. Helens' fire lookout was used until 1929; Mount Hood's was abandoned in 1935, after twenty years in operation. Both buildings were destroyed by the elements. The Mount Adams lookout was preserved because snow quickly filled the interior, which turned into ice and entombed the building. The crumbling structure, minus the cupola, remains to this day, but each year takes its toll. Will interior ice continue to anchor the wreckage in the decades to come? Or will a string of hot summers and dry winters leave the building high and dry, only to be swept off the mountain by the relentless hurricane force winds of winter? At least the thrilling stories will endure.

Chapter 6

Sulfur Mining

Those who worked on the mountain are reasonably sure that the descriptive phrase "cold as a well-digger's prat" must have originated on Mount Adams.

— Keith McCoy

The summit crater area of Mount Adams was an active sulfur and sulfate mineral mine from 1931 through 1937, although annual assessment work (at least a hundred dollars' worth) kept the mining claim alive until 1959. The mining venture failed because of the extreme difficulty of extracting and transporting the ore off the mountain. Yet it was a colorful chapter in the history of Mount Adams.

No one could tell the mining stories better than my old family friend Keith McCoy of White Salmon. McCoy had worked as a miner on the summit for two seasons and related his experiences in his 1987 book, *The Mount Adams Country*. But before he died in 2005, Keith told me some great stories in person. In the late 1990s and early 2000s, I interviewed two other former miners, Dick Mansfield and Bob Knoll, both in their eighties at the time.

During his last month as fire lookout in 1923, Art Jones investigated an exposure of yellowish, crumbly ground about a quarter-mile north of the lookout building. The mushy material contained sulfur crystals (elemental sulfur), which burned when he lit a small pile with a match. Jones carried several pounds of it back to his farm on his last trip down the mountain. Later he gave some to a friend, who burned it in his chicken coop to get rid of mites. The story caught the attention of a White Salmon entrepreneur, Wade H. Dean, who had known about an earlier discovery of sulfur and other mineral deposits high on the North Cleaver of Mount Adams. In 1927, Dean and a few associates formed the Glacier Mining Company and filed seventeen mineral claims on a two-hundred-ten-acre portion of the summit plateau, below and north of the true summit.

Finally in 1930, Jude Wang and Tony Guler of Trout Lake were hired to dig out the former Forest Service lookout and convert it into a cramped bunkhouse to house a mining crew. The building had completely filled with snow since its abandonment six years earlier. Wang and Guler at first backpacked many loads of supplies and materials to the summit, but Wade Dean would find a better way. He hired the best packer in the region, Jack Perry, to accomplish a feat that no one else had ever done: ride his horse with a pack string to the summit of Mount Adams. But before mineral ore could be hauled down the mountain, a horse trail had to be built on the steep section of Suksdorf Ridge below Pikers Peak. Little is known about its construction, but to this day sections of the trail are visible in late summer, when the rocky slopes become snow-free.

The mining crew consisted of up to eight strong young men recruited from local communities. They were offered $7.50 per day, plus room and board, an attractive wage during the Great Depression. Yet no job in the country would be tougher or more dangerous, or offer more cramped living quarters. The fourteen-foot-square former lookout building had room for only four bunks on the ground level, plus the cook's quarters in the six-foot-square cupola. The crew rotated twelve-hour shifts with four men working outside day and night, while the other four got some sleep and did various chores. Bob Knoll spent three seasons on the summit and worked nights out on the icecap. Knoll told me, "I jumped across crevasses at night in order to get to work!" During stormy periods, four of the men would also have to sleep on the floor. Yet

Once cooled, elemental sulfur vapor near Adams' summit formed yellow-colored crystals around the fumarole margins. (Dave Zimbelman)

even in the cramped space, cook Ollie Hensley somehow managed to feed every crew member who worked on the summit during the seven seasons of operation.

In the first year of mining, 1931, miners began digging a series of test pits in ice and mineral deposits on the edges of the icecap, as far as a half-mile north of the cabin. The crew boss was a geology graduate student, Claude S. Fowler, whose job was to survey and determine the extent and quality of the sulfur deposits. Miners used hand axes, picks, and extra-long shovels, and the man at the bottom of the pit would get soaked by the constant trickle of ice water. They rotated frequently, especially when they hit pockets of hydrogen sulfide gas. Gas masks were standard equipment, but not always used, causing a near fatality on one occasion. The deeper pits, up to five feet wide, required a tripod with a pulley and rope attached to a five-gallon pail for ore samples and ice debris. The deepest pit went down ninety feet in solid ice before reaching a sulfur deposit. "The ice at almost every depth held perfectly preserved specimens of butterflies," McCoy remembered.

A fumarole about a quarter-mile north of the cabin emitted 150°F hydrogen-sulfide gas and steam in 1934.

The gas vent was located on what the miners called South Island, which was a low ridge about 385 feet long and 100 feet wide. The rise marked the northeastern rim of a 1,600-foot-wide summit crater (unofficially named West Crater), which lies northwest of a smaller and more recent crater on the summit cone. A test pit that the miners had dug on South Island exposed a twenty-seven-foot-thick bed described as "sulphur ore," with 79 percent sulfur at a depth of four feet. By 1941, Mazamas climber Kenneth Phillips found that the fumarole had been reduced to a small, foot-wide, "slightly warm cavern with choking gas," which held four small birds killed by the gas. On the same day, other members of his party saw a flock of similar birds flying over the summit. The fumarole has long since cooled, and South Island has been covered by permanent snow and ice, probably since the late 1940s.

In 1998, when I interviewed Dick Mansfield, he was a wiry and amazingly fit eighty-five-year-old man living on the bluff in White Salmon with his younger wife, Adele. Mansfield had worked four seasons on Mount Adams from 1934 through 1937. He recalled a frightening incident that occurred at the bottom of a pit where the richest sulfur ore had been discovered.

Earl Hines and I had been trading off with the digging. It smelled like rotten eggs down there. The hole was about 28 feet deep when Earl passed out from the sulfur gasses. Andy Roth took off on a run to get gas masks that were left in the lookout building. The others lowered me down the hole using the tripod and pulley, but the rope was two feet short for me to reach Earl. I got gassed too, but was OK. They pulled Earl to the top, but his face scraped the sides of the pit all the way up. He came to eventually and then went down the mountain on a horse. Earl never returned to the job.

It's interesting how Keith McCoy's account of the same incident differs from Mansfield's. On a summer day in 1990, McCoy told me: "I, being the smallest of the crew, went down the safety rope to sit on the disabled man's shoulders and protect his head and face from jagged ice that jutted from the sides of the hole, while the other pulled us to the top." McCoy went on to relate that Russell Niblock (not Roth, as Mansfield asserted) ran off to get the masks, only to pass out after unwisely running

Jack Perry led more than four hundred summit trips, or about twelve hundred packhorse loads of fuel, tools, food, and other supplies. (Dick Mansfield Collection) *Below:* The mining crew of eight strong men worked twelve-hour shifts on the summit icecap. Extra-long shovels and plenty of grit were needed to dig prospecting pits up to ninety feet deep. (Dick Mansfield Collection)

a half-mile at 12,000 feet. He ended his account by relating that gas masks were used for the rest of the season, as well they should. According to the federal Agency for Toxic Substances, just a few breaths of air containing high levels of hydrogen sulfide gas can cause death.

In all, nine prospecting pits were dug. The ore sampled consisted of various proportions of native sulfur, sulfate minerals (mainly gypsum and alunite), kaolinite, silica, and residual andesite. The thickest mineral deposit measured was twenty-six feet deep. One ten-foot-deep pit at the upper edge of Adams Glacier yielded 44 percent sulfur at both top and bottom. Not far to the northwest, on the crest of the North Cleaver, sulfur averaged 50 percent. The purest was nearly 80 percent, close to the top of the pit where Earl Hines almost died. The miners also climbed into five different bergschrund crevasses to sample sulfur ore. Hydrogen-sulfide gas issued from nearly every crevasse bounding the sulfur field. The largest crevasse explored was at the head of Adams Glacier, in which ice overhung a fifty-foot vertical wall of rock. Blocks of ice were blasted with dynamite to expose a mineral deposit.

Because of the constant danger in the pits, Wade Dean came up with another system to locate and sample ore. In 1933, two drillers and a diamond-core drill rig were transported all the way from Alaska to the base of Mount

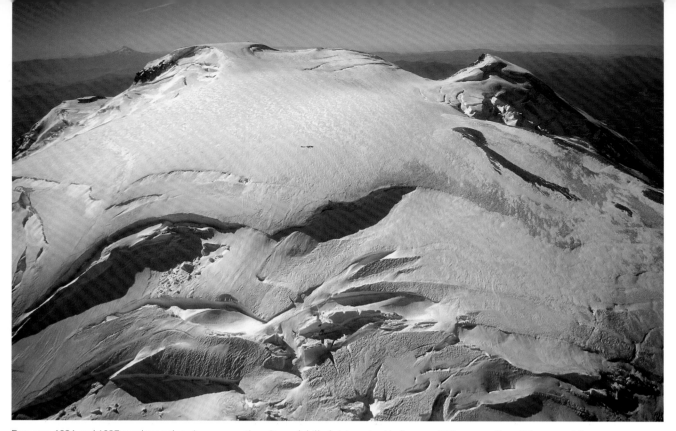

Between 1931 and 1937, workmen dug nine prospecting pits and drilled sixteen test holes on a 210-acre portion of the summit icecap.

Adams. Getting the twenty-two-hundred-pound gasoline-powered rig to the summit took four days of hard work. Mounted on a sled with a Ford engine, the rig winched its way up the long snow slopes in many slow stages. Using two hundred feet of half-inch rope, each stage required digging a three-foot-deep trench and burying a fir log as a "dead man" anchor. Another sled with drills and casing were also hauled up the slope. Heavy crowbars kept the sleds in position while the system was re-rigged for the next pull. Bob Knoll recalled that a horse wore itself out bringing up the crowbars, so the miners had to do the job themselves.

During the 1933–34 seasons, sixteen test holes (totaling 2,300 feet) were drilled into the summit icecap. Fourteen of the sixteen drill holes penetrated hydrothermally altered rock at the base of the ice, where potential ore deposits were located. The deepest hole drilled was 308 feet, but it failed to reach the bottom of the icecap.

Except during storms, the drill operated twenty-four hours a day in two twelve-hour shifts. About every hour, warm water was pumped into the drill holes to bring up slush from drilling through ice. The water also brought up sludge samples of pulverized rock, most of which contained a low percentage of sulfur. The diluted watery mix, however, could not be relied upon for determining actual proportions of minerals below the ice.

Each time the drill rig was moved, a large hole or "sump" had to be dug far enough uphill that a pipe could drain snowmelt water into two fifty-five-gallon drums next to the drill. A blowtorch was then used to warm the water in one of the drums (which doubled as a bathtub for some of the crew). For sun protection during their long days working, the miners smeared on a mix of iodine, cocoa butter, and olive oil. Based on old photos, some wore sunglasses while others did not.

At the end of the 1934 season, about sixty acres of the 210-acre claim area had been prospected. Claude Fowler (supervised by consulting geologist Edwin T. Hodge) analyzed all samples collected from pits, outcrops, crevasses, and drill holes. The locations were plotted on Fowler's topographic map titled "Sulphur Field of Mount Adams." With the average sulfur content in the ore sampled at 30 to 40 percent range, Hodge calculated the total sulfur present at more than six hundred thousand tons. At the same time, Fowler's estimate was about half as much, using 40 percent for the average sulfur content. In their

Using a diamond-core drill rig, the crew drilled up to 308 feet deep into the icecap. Most of the test holes reached potential ore deposits in hydrothermally altered rock. (Dick Mansfield Collection)

1934 reports, both Hodge and Fowler thought that the quantity of sulfur justified commercial exploitation, and Hodge even recommended mining all winter long in great caverns beneath the icecap.

Although the miners' focus was on sulfur, deposits of two sulfate minerals, alunite and gypsum, were also prospected and noted by the geologists. Hodge estimated quantities "at least twice that of sulfur" and "cheaper to mine." Mansfield told me that while sulfur was worth only $20 a ton in 1934, alunite was "going for $400 a ton." The richest alunite and gypsum deposits were found on the top of the North Cleaver and the unstable west-facing cliffs of the Avalanche/White Salmon Glacier headwall. Mansfield said "the alum [alunite] was 80 percent pure next to The Pinnacle."

During the years the mining company was active, Jack Perry led more than four hundred summit trips, or about twelve hundred packhorse loads of fuel, tools, food, and other supplies. The horses, in strings of three to seven, were then loaded with mineral ore for the return trip. Getting them down safely was a challenging job for the miners. According to Keith McCoy, the men used crampons and ropes to "save many horses which lost their footing . . . and went screaming into uncontrolled slides . . ." Remarkably only one horse was ever lost. Pack strings hauled the ore to the Timberline Shelter at 6,250 feet, where the road ended.

Carrying a thirty-pound pack and starting from the Timberline Shelter, Ed Knoll (a relative of Bob Knoll's) made the fastest climb to the summit in two hours and twenty-eight minutes. It's since been done in less than two hours, but probably not with a thirty-pound pack and not from the same starting point.

In my interviews with the three old-time miners, I asked each to describe the worst storm that they experienced on the summit. All spoke of the "granddaddy of them all" that hit in the afternoon in late summer of 1936. Six miners were working outside and saw the lightning storm approaching. They dropped their tools and took shelter in the cabin. The cook had also noted the black sky and prepared an early dinner. Tension mounted as they sat around the table, listening to the crashing of thunder that became deafening. When a lightning bolt struck the cabin, all seven men were knocked unconscious, and no one knew for how long. The cabin was filled with smoke and noise when they came to. A broom in the corner

In 1937, when the crew abandoned the building, they dragged a seven-hundred-pound bag of mineral ore off the mountain. (Dick Mansfield Collection)

was on fire, the table a mess, a metal dishpan warped, door hinges fused, cabin posts splintered, and an acrylic glass window shattered. Ollie Hensley, the cook, quickly grabbed two boxes of dynamite caps (which should have been stored in the outhouse) and threw them out the damaged door. Bob Knoll suffered the only injury, a burned buttock. He had been sitting on the diamond drill motor with a wrench in his back pocket. The storm returned an hour later when all were in their sleeping bags. McCoy wrote: "Those among us who hadn't learned to pray were fast learners."

The next day the crew picked up dynamite caps that were scattered all over the place. The cupola had been badly damaged, and many holes were burned in the metal roof flashing. It could have been far worse for the crew. Dick Mansfield described seeing an iron anchor bolt at the corner of the building that had become "a ball of fire" during the storm. That might have grounded some of the energy of the strike. Surprisingly, neither the mining company nor the Forest Service (in the 1920s) had properly grounded the lookout for protection from lightning strikes. In 1936, two sheds were built on the east side of the original lookout building for storage of drilling equipment, dynamite, tools, and other equipment.

Wade Dean had an engineer draw up plans for an aerial tramway with ore buckets to transport mineral ore from the summit of Adams down the south side to the J. Neils Lumber Company logging railroad. In 1936, Mansfield worked with surveyor Don Stevenson to map the thirteen-mile route. From Pikers Peak, the tramway would have followed a more-or-less straight line down Suksdorf Ridge, over South Butte, and across A G Aiken Lava Bed to the pine forests on the south slope of King Mountain at the 3,000-foot level. However, it was never built.

The whole mining project had been "iffy" due to a number of factors. Among them were financing issues, Dean's ownership of a telephone company, and the discovery of huge sulfur deposits on the Gulf Coast. Dean would soon call a halt to all active mining operations on Mount Adams.

In 1937, when the crew abandoned the summit lookout building, they dragged a huge canvas bag of ore off the mountain. The above photo in Mansfield's album shows the seven-hundred-pound bag at the edge at Pikers Peak and men guiding it with ropes. Details are incomplete, but somehow they got the cargo down to where horses could complete the transport.

Eventually ice would fill and prop up the battered summit lookout, minus the cupola. Without the anchoring ice, hurricane-force winds would have blown the building off the mountain long ago. But for how many more warm years? Likewise, the drill rig is encased in ice that filled the crumbling storage shed. The building is an archaeological site and is also registered as a National Historic Lookout.

The site of the old Timberline Shelter lies on a flat a few hundred feet below the intersection of the Round-the-Mountain Trail and South Climb Trail. Before the 2012 Cascade Creek Fire swept through the area, barely a trace of the three-sided shelter remained.

With climate warming and ever-thinning snow and ice fields on the summit and upper slopes of Mount Adams, it's near certain that new evidence of the sulfur mining and lookout era will be exposed. Tales of this fascinating era is a story in progress.

Top: At fourteen feet square, the former lookout cabin left little room for crew members, identified as "Roy, Bob, and Andy," to read or enjoy a pipe. (Dick Mansfield Collection) *Above:* A young miner takes a bath in water heated by blow torch. The warm water was pumped into drill holes to bring up sludge samples of ore. (Dick Mansfield Collection)

Chapter 7

The Lloyd Boys

A people who climb the ridges and sleep under the stars in high mountain meadows, who enter the forest and scale the peaks, who explore glaciers and walk ridges buried deep in snow—these people will give their country some of the indomitable spirit of the mountains.

— William O. Douglas

My twin brother Darvel and I were two years old in 1945 when our family moved to the Glenwood Valley at the base of Mount Adams. With meager savings, our parents put a down payment on eighty acres of second-growth ponderosa pine and meadowland about a mile from the small town of Glenwood, which was, and still is, a logging and farming community located on the northern edge of Camas Prairie. In the first summer and fall, the five of us, including older sister Christina, occupied a tent house hidden in the young pines. Our future home site was nearby on the edge of a lush, green meadow. Above the meadow only fifteen miles away loomed the rugged southeast face of Mount Adams.

With the help of local loggers, our father cleared an airstrip 200 feet wide and 2,000 feet long diagonally across the property. Our eighty-acre place was named Flying L Ranch, because Dad owned a Waco biplane and it allowed him to commute to his forestry job with Defiance Lumber Company in Tacoma. Mom had visions of a small dude ranch, and she hoped the airstrip would be used by fly-in guests.

At first, our parents rented an old bedbug-infested house in town during the winter of 1945–46. When spring arrived, local carpenters began construction of our large, odd-shaped house (now called "The Lodge" at the Flying L). The unusual building was designed by our grandfather Herman Dercum and was the talk of the town. A row of windows faced Mount Adams on the long side of the house. This design feature was unheard of locally. Homes in the valley always faced roads, never toward the mountain. The house was also unique because it was built on the far side of a meadow, a quarter-mile from the main gravel road called Mount Adams Highway.

A farmhouse-sized kitchen and a couple of rustic bedrooms had been completed by the fall of 1946. The kitchen, which doubled as a family room, had a Home Comfort wood stove for cooking, and it was the only source of heat for the long winters. Firewood filled much of the covered back porch. Two wood boxes near the kitchen stove had the seats that everyone wanted because winters were awfully harsh. Snow always piled five feet deep, and low temperatures to -20°F were common.

During 1947 construction work was concentrated on the big living room. Besides windows on both sides, it had redwood walls and a high ceiling held up by Douglas fir logs. At the far end was a massive fireplace made of Mount Adams andesite flagstone. The fireplace took several years to build, partly because Dad hauled the heavy rock down from the mountain only a few pieces at a time in the trunk of our '39 Chrysler sedan. The quarry at the 5,500-foot level near Bird Creek Meadows was a bone-jarring eighteen-mile drive each way. Some trips became family excursions with picnics at Bird Lake, allowing time for little boys and their sister to explore the area around the lake.

The ranch house was finished more or less in 1948, and outbuildings were soon to follow. I must say that no one ever thought of the place as a real dude ranch, even though three or four horses galloped around a "circle-acre" corral, and a couple of Hereford steers

fattened up in the front meadow. Many people with private planes landed on the airstrip. They picnicked and used our bathroom, but rarely stayed overnight. It would be ten years before our home place actually became a low-key guest ranch.

The long winters in the Glenwood Valley were especially severe during the 1940s and '50s. We were always outside doing something in the snow, such as sledding or building an igloo. The great blizzard of January 13, 1950, set records for snow and cold in the Northwest. In Glenwood it snowed six feet with deeper drifts, and the temperature fell to -39°F. Darvel, Christina, and I were among a number of school kids who got stranded in town. Generous people living near the school provided us food and shelter. Following the storm, our parents rode into town and brought us home on horseback.

We tried out Cub Scouts for a little while, but it was our father who taught us how to take care ourselves in the wilds. He would bring us along when he cruised

Top: A reproduction of Mom's woodblock print shows the Flying L Ranch from the front meadow in the early 1960s. (Ilse Lloyd) *Above:* The Lloyd twins pose with Tuffy. Dad helped us build the igloo. (Les Lloyd)

Top: Mount Adams' southeast face rises two vertical miles above the "East 40" meadow of the Flying L. *Above:* A typical late-1940s midwinter scene shows Dad's '39 Chrysler, unfinished buildings, and a visiting neighbor. (Les Lloyd)

timber in forested areas near the Klickitat Canyon and elsewhere. With him, we hiked through rough country with no roads or trails, and learned the use of map and compass at a young age. We slept under the stars frequently, even though dew would always soak our sleeping bags. In rainy weather we would rig a tarp, which meant that keeping dry was almost impossible if the rain lasted for very long.

We first climbed Mount Adams as ten-year-olds with our father in the summer of 1953. Back then the standard climbing route started near Morrison Creek at 6,700 feet, about two miles beyond today's South Climb Trailhead. Our first time up the mountain, we camped in a sandy spot at about 9,000 feet, but without a tent, and dust blew in our faces during the night. The next day, fierce winds forced us to crawl on our bellies across the flat above Pikers Peak (the south false summit) at 11,657 feet. We were woefully ill-equipped for the weather, wearing denim jackets and cotton gloves. I remember being miserable from the cold and altitude, yet the thrill of reaching the top dominated our thoughts. That excitement showed in our pencil sketches of Mount Adams, which our mother saved, and are still in my file. We were hooked on climbing.

A year later, in 1954, Dad led us on our first climb of Mount Hood. He had climbed it first in 1922 as a teenager and later did "seat-of-the-pants" climbs on other Oregon volcanoes, and in the Olympic Mountains of Washington state. At Crater Rock on Mount Hood, strong hydrogen sulfide gas emissions made Darvel and me nauseous; but the sickness lasted only while we were in the area of fumaroles. Dad knew enough about safety to rope us up when we climbed, but he carried the only ice axe. Midway up what's now called the West Crater Rim route on Hood, he poked one foot through the snow bridge of a hidden crevasse (now called the Bergshrund). Dad could have easily fallen into the black void and dragged us down with him. As we climbed the steep slope above the crevasse, I could see a wooden sign on a single post at the top. I imagined the words would say "Summit of Mount Hood," but when we finally reached the sign at the summit crest, the words were: "Keep off the Grass." With Dad's camera, I took a picture of him and Darvel on the summit. It was one of my first mountain photographs.

Our new schoolteacher, Bob Pfeifer, was an experienced mountain climber who knew technical skills that exceeded our father's. In late spring 1955, Pfeifer brought us along as twelve-year-olds for a climb of Mount St. Helens. We camped along the Toutle River in a grove of large, old-growth Douglas firs, and then snowshoed from Spirit Lake to the Longview Ski Club cabin on the north side of the volcano. In the morning we started to climb under an overcast sky. It began to snow hard above the Dogs Head, but because there was little wind, we continued to climb. In the whiteout I could dimly make out the edges of crevasses above us, thinking that each one was the rim of the crater (which on St. Helens was called the False Summit). We finally turned back at about the 9,000-foot level, which was a higher turnaround than all the other climbing teams on the mountain that day. I remember it as a surreal experience. We never did tell our mother the whole truth about that climb.

Whatever miseries we had on the three "Guardian" volcanoes were soon forgotten; mountains and climbing

Top: At age ten in the summer of 1953, we prepare to make our first climb of Mount Adams with our father. (Les Lloyd) *Above:* Posing on top of the old lookout (cupola in the background), we brace in the icy cold wind, woefully ill-equipped with our denim jackets and cotton gloves. (Les Lloyd)

A small lake on the western rim of the crater in 1958 was caused by fumarole activity. My photo is the only documented evidence of such a lake on the summit of Adams, although Native American legends tell of a large one.

were all we could think about. Bob Pfeifer took us on a couple of other tough scrambles and climbs during 1955. One was a rarely hiked loop on the southeast side of Mount Adams. Starting at Bird Creek Meadows, we skirted lower Mazama Glacier and climbed to the top of the Ridge of Wonders at 8,450 feet. The view of Klickitat Glacier was spectacular. With my first camera, a Kodak Brownie Holiday, I photographed Pfeifer, his son (an older teen), and my brother Darvel with the glacier in the background. It was the same spot on the Ridge of Wonders where C. E. Rusk and W. D. Lyman rhapsodized about the view sixty years earlier.

Descending the narrow spine of the ridge, Pfeifer taught us the Dulfersitz rappel and how to belay another climber with a rope. After reaching Little Mount Adams, we dropped down to Hellroaring Meadow, had a break at Heart Lake, and hiked back to Bird Creek Meadows on an old sheepherder's trail through old-growth mountain hemlock. We had accomplished a rugged, off-trail scramble loop that's seldom done, even today. On this trip, too, I got hooked on photography and have rarely been without a camera ever since.

After these adventures Darvel and I pored through pages of our parents' books, especially *Tales of a Western Mountaineer* by C. E. Rusk, *Annapurna* by Maurice Herzog, *Book of Marvels* by Richard Halliburton, and *The Guardians of the Columbia*, by John H. Williams.

Published in 1912, *The Guardians* is filled with photos showing Adams, Hood, and St. Helens draped by glaciers far thicker and longer than they are today. Women climbers wore mid-calf black skirts for climbing, horses provided access to the climbs' base, and giant trees ruled the forests. Early in the book, Williams describes the trio of volcanoes from the vantage of the heights above Portland: "Dominating all are the snow-peaks, august sentinels upon the horizon. Spirit-like, they loom above the soft Oregon haze, their glaciers signaling from peak to peak, and their shining summits bidding the sordid world below to look upward."

We were lured mostly to the three Guardian volcanoes because of their proximity, but from 1956 to 1965 our glacier climbs on Mount Adams and a number of other Cascade peaks had to be squeezed in between periods of living and traveling in other parts of the world. Darvel and I lived in Taiwan for two years (our father was part of the Aid for International Development program), went to high school together in Portland, and then ended up attending colleges on opposite sides of the country.

Meantime, in 1957, U.S. Supreme Court Justice William O. Douglas and his wife Mercedes purchased a summer home near Glenwood, just a mile up the road from our family's Flying L Ranch. "Justice Bill" (as we called him) and "Mercy" became close family friends. He frequently used our airstrip for chartered single-engine plane flights to different parts of Washington and Oregon. From his Glenwood home in 1960, Douglas wrote *My Wilderness: The Pacific West*, with a beautiful chapter about Mount Adams.

While serving as an associate justice of the U.S. Supreme Court, the longest tenure in history, Douglas wrote twelve hundred legal decisions and thirty-four books, plus countless articles in magazines. His true passion was the American wilderness, and as an activist to protect wild areas, he was one of the nation's all-time champions.

In summer 1960, Darvel and I had completed our junior year of high school living in Portland, and then spent the summer hitchhiking around Europe with two buddies on less than five dollars a day. The Douglases, who hadn't left for Glenwood yet, invited us to spend a few nights at their beautiful Georgetown, D. C., home. We threw our sleeping bags on their lawn and woke up to a *Washington Post* reporter and photographer. The story and photo made the front pages of the *Washington Post* and Portland's *Sunday Oregonian*. We couldn't understand why it was such a big deal, since we had camped under the stars countless times on friends' lawns and, of course, in the wilds.

A day later on that trip, Dad's 1957 Ford had a major engine seizure while heading north toward Idlewild Airport in New York. After a phone call, Justice Bill offered his official Supreme Court car and driver to deliver us to the International airport in time to make our Icelandic Airlines flight. The driver was a wonderful, kind black man, and I regret not remembering his name. He arranged for a major repair of our Ford while we were gone. We could not have done our Europe trip without Mercedes and Justice Bill Douglas rescuing us from that untimely New Jersey Turnpike breakdown.

Top: On another climb of Adams in 1958, Dad prepares our gear at timberline. An international forester by profession, he had "seat of the pants" climbing experience. *Above:* Justice William O. Douglas visits with Dad, Mercedes Douglas, Darvel, and other friends in the big kitchen of the Flying L in 1959.

The next summer after high school, in 1961, we assisted an NBC-TV crew who filmed Justice Douglas on Mount Adams with boy actor Richard Thomas for a children's educational television series called *1, 2, 3 Go!* The crew stayed at the Flying L Ranch and did their filming in Bird Creek Meadows, where Douglas told the young actor about the glory of mountains and the importance of their protection in a wild state. He described the long-lasting damage that sheep had done to the meadows in the early decades of the 1900s. In the nationally televised program, the lad Thomas was whisked instantly to Mount Adams from Manhattan.

The big living room at the Flying L hasn't changed much—from the time we were kids, to this early 1980s photo, to the present day.

Only weeks later it was I who had a view of Manhattan from a dorm window on the north shore of Long Island, where between fall 1961 and summer 1965, I attended the U.S. Merchant Marine Academy in Kings Point, New York. Darvel attended Oregon State University and majored in geology.

On three different occasions during my time on the East Coast, I was a special guest of Justice Douglas for hikes with him along the historic C&O Canal, which began near his home in Georgetown. The first hike was on Thanksgiving Day 1961, when, in my own words (Mom saved the letter I wrote after my four-day stay), "Justice Bill and I took a little walk of 10 miles up the old canal towpath." In the letter I added: "You can bet I learned a lot about everything on that jaunt." For one, Douglas told me about the 185-mile C&O Canal's history and how seven years earlier (in 1954) he was instrumental in saving the canal and its Towpath from being bulldozed into a highway. Later in the afternoon for "the wonderful

turkey dinner," only four of us were present, including the justice, his wife Mercedes, and her lovely daughter Joannie Davidson.

Justice Bill invited me on two of his annual Reunion Hikes of the C&O Canal Association. For the late April 1963 occasion (only seven months before President John F. Kennedy's was assassinated), Douglas arranged for a black limousine to meet me at the Washington, D.C., bus station. An obviously important friend of his was sitting in the backseat: Secretary of Agriculture Orville Freeman, the former governor of Minnesota. What a warm and likable man. I ended up spending the weekend with Freeman and his teenaged son Michael, and I learned for the first time about the proposed wilderness act, which he and his huge Department of Agriculture would administer.

A year later, under President Lyndon Baines Johnson's administration, the Wilderness Act of 1964 became law, protecting 42,411 acres of Mount Adams. Within six years, the mountain and its wilderness would define my way of life.

Top left: We assisted an NBC-TV crew in 1961 as they filmed Justice Douglas with boy actor Richard Thomas. A buddy, Ken Pinnon, was holding the clapper. (Michael Davidson)

Top right: Photographed at the Flying L front porch around 1957, Mom loved horses, was an accomplished artist, and a gentle, kind person. (Darryl Lloyd Collection)

Left: In 1961, after graduating from Benson High School, we guided three Portland Rose Festival princesses and a buddy up Mount Adams. This shot was taken after the climb. (Les Lloyd)

Chapter 8

Sharing the Mountain

Earth and sky, woods and fields, lakes and rivers, the mountain and the sea, are excellent schoolmasters, and teach some of us more than we can ever learn from books.

— John Lubbock

My life changed because of my friendship and association with Justice William O. Douglas and other nationally known leaders, such as David Brower and Orville Freeman. Their powerful advocacy for the protection and preservation of wilderness had a huge influence on much of what I've accomplished and treasured since my undergraduate years. In other words, meeting those architects of the American wilderness movement left profound and lasting impressions that would carry through my many decades of work to share and conserve Mount Adams and other wild areas.

Douglas stoked the fire in me in April 1965, when he invited me for another C&O Canal Reunion Hike. I was his special guest along with then-Sierra Club Executive Director David Brower and Douglas's law clerk, Jerry Falk. That was the first time I met David Brower, an association entirely due to the good fortune of knowing Justice Bill. The three of us—Brower, Falk, and I—would stick together for the long weekend. Our hike on the canal Towpath from Dam 4 to the James Rumsey Memorial Bridge was thronged with seven hundred people, including Secretary of the Interior Stewart Udall and a host of conservation leaders. During the lunch break, I stood next to Douglas, Udall, and Brower, whose heated discussions centered on the proposed Marble Canyon Dam of the Colorado River. I would later visit David Brower in San Francisco while he was putting together the first Sierra Club exhibit-format book on the Glen Canyon.

Darvel and I, the mountain men, became mariners during wartime because we loved ships during our travels as young teens. After I graduated from Kings Point in 1965 (and Darvel from Oregon State University), we went to sea in different roles as Naval Reserve officers. Darvel served in Vietnam as the supply officer on the USS *Henry County*, an LST (landing ship tank) from World War II. His ship played a big role in amphibious operations along the Vietnam coast. I got civilian seafaring jobs as a licensed mate on oceanographic research vessels operated separately by the University of Washington, Lamont Geological Observatory (Columbia University), and Texas A&M University. While seafaring, I continued to add exotic places and experiences to my list of travels, including the Peruvian Andes, Galapagos, Tahiti, and the northeast coast of Australia. A friend in the scientific crew joined me on climbs on active volcanoes in Mexico and Costa Rica, and an attempt on Mount Fuji in Japan. To advance my license, I needed sea time on larger ships, so I then sailed as second mate on bulk ore carriers between the Gulf Coast, Hawaii, and the Columbia River.

In the fall and winters of 1967 and 1968, Darvel and I shared an apartment in Boulder as graduate students in geography at the University of Colorado. We had been away from the Northwest for a long time and missed seeing our parents and spending time on Mount Adams. The mountain was on both of our minds when we enrolled in a cartography class together. For the term project, I made the first and possibly only scale model of Mount Adams. Such a model can now be done with computers, Styrofoam, and specialized 3-D printers, but during the golden age of cartography almost a half-century ago, the process involved hundreds of hours of effort and a variety of materials, including clay, green soap, plaster of Paris, dental tools, and watercolor paints.

In the same class, Darvel painted a large pictorial map of the Guardian volcanoes: Adams, St. Helens, and Hood. It was an oblique, aerial view looking eastward up the Columbia River Gorge. The mountains and other features were identified on the framed painting. It now sits in a closet of his Portland home, and my Mount Adams model is on a bench in my garage, badly in need of a paint job and a new base.

For his master's thesis, Darvel took on a year-round study of Isabelle Glacier, located near the Continental Divide in Colorado's Front Range. Weather instruments on the glacier had to be serviced regularly, and that meant several days of winter mountaineering each month. I was handy and happy to assist, but didn't bargain on our first experience at surviving Arctic conditions in a vicious blizzard. We skied in and camped halfway to the glacier near a frozen lake; and I broke my Japanese ice axe trying to chop through lake ice to reach water. That night the temperature fell to around -30°F, and 60 mph winds, with higher gusts, repeatedly crushed our (borrowed) McKinley tent. With wind chill reaching -75°F, we took turns going out into the storm's fury at night to re-rig the tent. We wore facemasks and all the layers of wool and down that we had. According to present-day charts, frostbite in those conditions would occur on exposed flesh in about five minutes. The next day we returned to Boulder, exhausted from the harrowing night.

Top: A Mount Adams Wilderness Institute (MAWI) group of the mid-1970s prepares to continue the traverse of the east side. I'm at far right with an eighty-pound pack. (Bob Branscomb) *Above:* Darvel and Darryl pose on the summit of Mount Adams on the last day of a MAWI session in the early 1970s. (Darryl Lloyd Collection)

Top: A 1992 photo shows an early-summer view of Mount Adams from the Flying L lawn. About the only difference from the 1950s is the size of the trees. *Above:* Relaxing with a pipe, after guiding a group to Avalanche Valley in the early 1970s. (Susan Lloyd)

On another January day not nearly as stormy or cold, Darvel cheated death in a slab avalanche while returning from servicing instruments on Isabelle Glacier. The two of us were traversing across moderately steep slopes on Niwot Ridge to reach a mountain research field station, where we had camped. The slide broke at 12,300 feet and carried him about a thousand feet down a steep, snow-filled chute. Darvel managed to get on top of the soft slab after it started moving, but was churned underneath when it broke up. Fortunately he came out on top just before the avalanche stopped. I immediately glissaded down the chute to see if he was okay. Darvel suffered serious bruises, but no broken bones. As darkness fell, we made it safely back to the field station, a small cabin at 11,600 feet, which was maintained by the Institute for Arctic and Alpine Research. Important lessons we learned: Carry a rope for winter climbs to the glacier, and at all costs avoid avalanche terrain. At least have a secure belay before crossing a gully or slope that might slide.

A severe midsummer snowstorm pins a MAWI group to their tents for several days. High winds drifted snow several feet deep in places.

In spring 1970, Darvel, my wife Susan, and I reunited at our parents' Flying L Ranch in Glenwood and founded the Mount Adams Wilderness Institute (MAWI). The institute turned out to be an amazingly successful ten-year-long program, combining wilderness mountaineering instruction with natural history. It was an idea that we had been tossing around during graduate school. We saw a need for an alternative to the longer outdoor programs already offered by Outward Bound and National Outdoor Leadership School. Our program was first billed as "a two-week wilderness, climbing, and educational experience for boys." Sessions would include mostly off-trail backpacking around Mount Adams, traveling on glaciers, exploring tundra areas and cinder cones, and climbing a summit by the Mazama Glacier route. We threw in survival skills and interpretation of the mountain environment. The charge was only two hundred and fifty dollars for two weeks, including all food, equipment, lodging, and transportation.

During MAWI's first summer, we held three fourteen-day sessions on Mount Adams; but because of our late start, only about a dozen teenage boys participated. One boy from Glenwood (on a full scholarship) had to be evacuated at the halfway point due to severe foot blisters. Otherwise, the round-the-mountain trips went well, and everyone made the summit by the Mazama Glacier route. With the help of a filmmaker, we produced a twenty-minute, 16mm film called *High Adventure of Mount Adams*, using Frederick Delius's *Florida Suite* for background music. The boys were enthusiastic about everything related to climbing and off-trail exploration, but they were far more interested in telling one-upmanship stories than learning the names of flowers or how volcanoes work. We vowed to include girls in all future programs.

In fall 1970, I was admitted to graduate school at the University of Rhode Island, and the following June, I earned a Master of Marine Affairs degree, emphasizing marine geology and geography. I had some spare time that year to promote our mountaineering school, so I drove up through New England and gave Mount Adams slide shows at private high schools.

Top: A MAWI group in the late 1970s descends Rusk Glacier, after ice-climbing instruction and practice on seracs, visible at left.
Above: Devils Gardens is an area of high alpine tundra with scattered, house-size blocks of brecciated clasts. An immense Holocene debris avalanche from the Wilson Glacier headwall created the "gardens." (Darvel Lloyd)

My last visit with Justice William O. Douglas was in 1971, while still in grad school in Rhode Island. Susan and I drove down to Washington, D. C., parked in the U.S. Supreme Court basement (by earlier arrangement), and were escorted to Douglas's chambers. We talked mostly about Mount Adams, since all of us shared such an intense interest in the mountain.

We met Darvel again at the Flying L Ranch in June 1971, and that summer we held four two-week sessions (or "mini-expeditions") on Mount Adams. We found that including girls made the trips much more fun and stimulating for everyone. The teens called Darvel and me "Oofl No. 1" and "Oofl No. 2," meaning "Our old fearless leader," even though we were only twenty-eight at the time.

A major storm hit us in late August 1971. Our last group for the summer was setting up tents at Sunrise Camp, the 8,300-foot saddle below Mazama Glacier. The summit climb was planned for the next day, but we realized that our tents were inadequate for such a storm. We had everyone pack up and head down the mountain as quickly as possible. Most of the people got soaked in the driving rain by the time we reached a grove of whitebark pines just below timberline. Darvel and I built a big fire from dead branches. Everyone got warmed up, had a hot meal, and weathered the stormy night in substandard

I pose in front of an unusual crevasse on Mount Shuksan in Washington's North Cascades. (Darvel Lloyd)

tents. With the storm showing no signs of abating the next morning, we packed up and headed down to meet Susan with the van at the Bird Creek Meadows trailhead. We returned to the Flying L for hot showers, "real food," and soft beds. Later we learned that two Outward Bound participants died of hypothermia in the same storm on their "solo" in the Three Sisters Wilderness of central Oregon.

We opened the Institute to admit adults in summer 1972 and held four two-week sessions. On the last day of the second session, July 28, 1972, we heard that our dad and two others had died in a canoe accident on the coast of British Columbia. It occurred as he and three passengers were headed into spectacular Bute Inlet in his forty-foot Philippine outrigger canoe, *Tango*. Large whirlpools and waves capsized the canoe in the notorious Aaron Rapids. The only survivor was Pat Dickerman, editor of *Adventure Trip Guide* in New York. Mom would have been on board, but she had had to return to the ranch for that week. Dad's body was never recovered. At his memorial, I said, "He really lived, and he really died." He was sixty-seven years old, and his life as an international forester would make a worthy biography.

Portions of our third session in August 1972 were filmed for an hour-long television show in a series called *Exploration Northwest* hosted by Don McCune of Seattle's KOMO-TV. The first half-hour segment of the two-part series featured our preparations at the ranch, followed by a day with the group at Bird Creek Meadows and a short history of Mount Adams. For Part Two of the show, on the tenth day of our round-the-mountain trek, Don and his film crew of two joined our group in Avalanche Valley. The three stayed with us for the rugged east side traverse and Mazama Glacier climb. But the climb had to be cut short of the summit as rain and thick clouds swept over the mountain.

Because of our growing reputation and nationwide promotion, MAWI filled eight sessions in 1973. Darvel and I each led four trips, alternating in length between two weeks and ten days. We hired assistants and limited group size to no more than ten participants, which conformed to the Forest Service's new wilderness regulations. We joined the adjunct faculty of Central Washington State University and offered upper-division (400-level) college credit through the extension division. This made our Institute program very attractive to high school teachers. By then Susan and I had designed and built a home on property adjacent to the Flying L Ranch.

Our 1973 brochure emphasized our new direction and priorities. (This was the last year that we used campfires for cooking.)

In addition to safe, responsible mountaineering and wilderness travel, a major goal of the Institute is to instill an appreciation for the mountain's fascinating natural and human history, and to share a deep respect for the area's preservation. On-site informal discussions are held daily, pursuing such topics as glacier behavior (what makes some of them advance and others retreat?), volcanic history (will the mountain erupt again?), lava flow comparisons (recent and old), timberline ecology (what governs the tree line?), and mountain weather (when to turn back). Around the campfire, topics of discussion might include Indian legends, man's impact on the wilderness, avalanches or historical climbing accounts.

In a MAWI newsletter dated February 15, 1975, I wrote that "all ten sessions were booked up last year by people from across the United States, as well as Canada and Mexico." We had experienced exceptionally stormy weather conditions in 1974, and there was an all-time record high snowpack in the Washington Cascades. On the summit climb of my second two-week session, we followed day-old elk tracks up Mazama Glacier. At Pikers Peak, we spotted two bull elk on the flat below the summit cone—a most amazing and likely never-before-or-since sighting. The elk had large antler racks but were too far away to get good photos. We unintentionally spooked them into heading across the heavily crevassed area of the upper Klickitat Glacier. I often wondered if they got off the mountain alive, but the likelihood of it is slim.

The Institute was a remarkable ten-year success story. At the end of 1979, the last year of operation, a total of seventy-five sessions were held on Mount Adams. Sessions were booked up every year except for 1970–71. The only serious accident was a broken leg when a Canadian man jumped a small crevasse and landed wrong. I led forty-four sessions, including eleven that I co-led with Darvel. My days and nights on Mount Adams during the decade

Traversing the north side during a two-week MAWI session in 1972, we were filmed for a two-part KOMO-TV show in Seattle, called *Exploration Northwest*.

came to around four hundred sixty-five, plus many more during off-season glacier climbs and backcountry ski trips. Darvel's total came to thirty-nine sessions, or about four hundred thirty days and nights on the mountain.

In 1977–78, Darvel directed the Mount Adams Young Adult Conservation Corps in Trout Lake. He moved to Colorado, and from 1978–81 directed the Keystone Science School (then called the Keystone Environmental Education Center).

During the 1970s and 1980s, Darvel and I accomplished a respectable number of mountaineering ascents elsewhere in the Cascades, Stuart Range, and Rocky Mountains. Both of us were members of the American Alpine Club and active with mountain search-and-rescue organizations. I participated with the Alpinees of Hood River, Oregon, while Darvel had different experiences with the Summit County Rescue Group based at Frisco, Colorado.

All MAWI sessions scheduled for 1980 were booked solid when Mount St. Helens erupted cataclysmically on May 18. The eruptions of 1980 and indefinite administrative closure of Mount Adams through 1981 ended the institute.

But inspired by the great conservationists like William O. Douglas, I continued to campaign on behalf of Mount Adams, teach, and lead groups into its wilderness. In the mid-1970s, Darvel and I formed "Friends of Pahto" at the Flying L Ranch. In the years ahead, Friends would have dormant periods, and I would return to seafaring for a period during the 1980s as a ship's captain. But almost a lifetime of sharing Mount Adams, and wild areas elsewhere, is the legacy I hope is remembered.

Participants in MAWI learn about safe glacier travel while negotiating crevasses on Wilson Glacier. (Darvel Lloyd)

PART TWO

MOUNTAIN SCIENCE

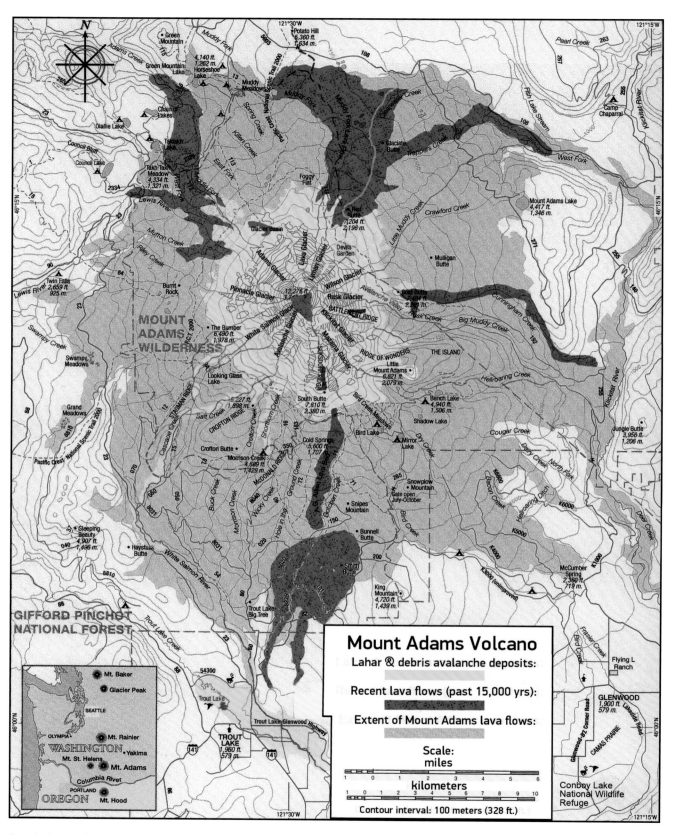

A geologic map shows the eighteen-mile-diameter base of the Mount Adams stratovolcano, including the most recent lava flows, debris avalanches, and lahar deposits. (Map source: Wes Hildreth and Judy Fierstein, USGS)

Chapter 9

Mount Adams Volcano

*This scarred old volcano, in its entirety—this shapeless mass—combines all the elements that go
to make a scene of noble, rugged, untamed grandeur.*

— C. E. Rusk

Two of my favorite authors, C. E. Rusk and Justice William O. Douglas, loved and wrote about Mount Adams, and both declared it an extinct volcano. It's an understandable mistake; little was known about the eruptive history of the "scarred old" mountain before the early 1980s. A half a century ago, well after Rusk and Douglas wrote their books, Darvel and I were both in graduate school working toward master's degrees in different fields of geography. By then we knew the mountain was dormant, definitely not extinct, and that it had erupted both young and old andesite lavas. But we had little idea about ages or many other aspects of its geologic history until 1995, when the USGS volcanologists published a massive research study that illuminated the whole story.

In eruptive volume, Mount Adams is the largest stratovolcano (a composite of lavas and fragmental material) in Washington and Oregon. It stands atop eroded remains of older structures that date back more than a half-million years. Volcanologists now view Mount Adams as potentially active, or simply *active*, meaning it has erupted in the last ten thousand years (since the Ice Age) and is likely to erupt again. The last eruption was about a thousand years ago, although inconclusive evidence indicates an eruption on the east flank might have occurred less than five hundred years ago. Geologists say the volcano's magma plumbing system shows no signs of shutting down.

Scientific discussions of past and future volcanic activity on Mount Adams are based on the monumental work of USGS volcanologists Wes Hildreth and Judy Fierstein. They deserve special recognition for their roles in the history of Mount Adams exploration. During the 1980s and early 1990s, Hildreth and Fierstein spent a total of three hundred eighty long, hard days crisscrossing the five-hundred-square-mile Mount Adams Volcanic Field. Their fieldwork resulted in detailed mapping, compositional data, ages, and volume estimates of one hundred thirty-two separate eruptive units, most of which make up the central volcano of Mount Adams.

I first met Wes Hildreth on the mountain in the summer of 1981; he was hammering on a contorted dacite lava outcrop above Bird Creek Meadows. He and Judy were frequent guests at my home in Glenwood during their years of fieldwork on the mountain, and we have been good friends ever since. In 2018, they were continuing their volcano research worldwide as two of the most productive scientists in the long history of the USGS.

Volcanologists describe the enormous bulk of Mount Adams above 7,000 feet or so as "youthful" relative to the age of the much broader half-million-year-old edifice beneath it. The asymmetrical "modern cone" was built during a prolonged eruptive phase from about 40,000 to 15,000 years ago, during the last part of the Pleistocene (Ice Age), when ice covered up to 80 percent of the 230-square-mile volcano. Glaciers that filled valleys as low as 3,500 feet began to recede only at the end of this eruptive period.

Magma moved up through a central vent system in intermittent spurts during the 25,000-year episode. There is no evidence of the most violent type of eruptions (Plinian) or pyroclastic flows on Mount Adams. Eruptions of rubbly andesite lava (56–62 percent silica) were mostly effusive and non-explosive—in marked

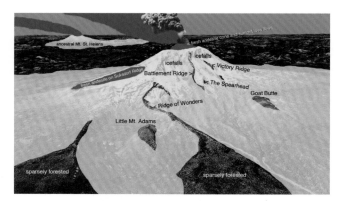

The mountain might have looked somewhat like this around 15,000 years ago, near the end of the Ice Age. Eruptions were building the summit cone as well as lower Suksdorf Ridge. (Base map data: Google Earth)

World-renowned volcanologist Wes Hildreth samples twenty-four Mount Adams andesitic ash layers from a collapsed stream bank near Bird Creek Meadows. Eight thousand years of eruptive history was exposed.

contrast to explosive Mount St. Helens and the relatively gentle Hawaiian type of eruptions. They were also much different than Mount Hood's lava dome cycles of repeated growth-and-collapse into pyroclastic flows. On Adams, with glaciers much larger than they are today, lava flowing onto snow and ice shattered into rubble, and oxidized to a reddish-brown color by hot steam. Many flows became lava debris avalanches as they disintegrated over cliffs or steep ice. Thin layers of harder, dark-gray lava are sandwiched between stratified cinders, agglutinates—which are cinders and molten fragments called "bombs," fused by their own heat—and breccia (lava blocks in an ash matrix). Over the millennia that followed, glacial erosion exposed these multiple lava flows almost like growth rings; and the layers are easily visible during summer seasons on the sides of Battlement Ridge and headwalls of Lava, Pinnacle, and Mazama glaciers.

Adams' structure was described on one online source as made of "several overlapping cones." Actually, inside is a single, long-lived central vent system with branching vents on the mountain's flanks. Lavas from the mountain's flank bear a chemical composition similar to those from the massive central vent. The volcano's exceptionally broad, humpbacked profile, when viewed from the east (Yakima Valley) or the west (Mount St. Helens), can be attributed to shifting summit craters and flank vents as high as 9,400 feet on the south side and 8,400 feet on the northeast side.

Because of the shifting eruptive vents, the summit is well over a mile wide in a north–south direction. And while summit lavas erupted roughly 15,000 years ago, fumarole activity continues under the icecap even now. Lavas exposed in late summer take up less than a half-square-mile on the south and west sides of the summit, and on the crest of the North Cleaver. Most of the summit lavas that we see have been altered by hot, steamy fumaroles into masses of multicolored and crumbly minerals, exposed on cliffs and at the margins of the ice-filled craters.

A massive ice cap now covers much of the summit area of Mount Adams, yet the contours of several craters are revealed in aerial photos. The main crater, which I call West Crater, is about 1,600 feet wide and located in a depression northwest of the highest point. The true

Above around 7,000 feet, most of Mount Adams' bulk is "youthful," having been constructed over a long eruptive period, from about 40,000 to 15,000 years ago.

summit is a stubby, half-mile-wide fragmental cone. An 800-foot-wide shallow crater slopes toward the south, with about a third of the crater eroded away. The last minor steam explosions from the fragmental cone could have occurred about 5,000 years ago, wrote Hildreth and Fierstein in their 1997 USGS paper, "Recent eruptions of Mount Adams . . ."

Central to their research on the most recent eruptions is a remarkable volcanic ash deposit cross-section, located on a meadow bench below Hellroaring Viewpoint near Bird Creek Meadows. Darvel and I were first to scrape clean and photograph the collapsed, six-foot-high stream bank that exposed nearly 8,000 years of ash layers from Adams, St. Helens, and Mazama (now called Crater Lake). Hildreth called it "an extraordinary inclusive sequence of (eruption) fallout layers." In 1992 he sampled twenty-four andesitic ash layers from Mount Adams eruptions. Hildreth approximated the age by comparing the sequences to layers from Mount St. Helens, which were

well-known and much thicker. He found four thin layers of Mount Adams ash sandwiched between 2,500- and 500-year-old St. Helens layers. The youngest Adams ash, he estimated, was deposited about a thousand years ago.

A cone of reddish scoria (dark lava trapped with bubbles) at 8,400 feet on Battlement Ridge might even be much younger. Two half-mile-long lava flows erupted from the vent. The southerly flow ends at 7,200 feet alongside Klickitat Glacier, sandwiched in what looks like a Little Ice Age moraine. Hildreth and Fierstein found no soil, regional ash, or carbon deposits on or around either lava flow. They wrote: "Because the overlying till is probably no older than a few centuries, the lava could be one of the youngest at Mount Adams." Their words have intrigued me since I first read them in 1997. I've climbed across the flow many times while backpacking across the east side, and I've always hoped that a geologist will find a way to date the Battlement Ridge eruption with greater accuracy. In reviewing this chapter, Hildreth wrote in the

My rough sketch shows some features of the mile-wide summit area.

Left: The reddish cone on Battlement Ridge is likely the youngest vent on Mount Adams. Nearby is a remnant of one of the oldest lava flows: The Spearhead, oxidized an orange-brown color. *Right:* On the northeast side, Red Butte (bottom center) erupted basalt about 14,000 years ago, resulting in an eight-mile-long lava flow. To the right of the scoria cone is a fissure zone of the longer 6,000-year-old Muddy Fork andesite lava flow.

margin: "Wish I were *certain* the till is Little Ice Age." In the meantime, we can only speculate. It's possible that the andesite of Battlement Ridge is younger than 500 years old, because Mount St. Helens ash from a large 1482 AD eruption could not be found on top of the fresh lava flow.

During an interval from about 7,000 to 3,500 years ago, within the time frame of occupation by the earliest Native people, a series of thick andesite lava flows issued from vents near tree line on Mount Adams. The dark, blocky lava rumbled for miles into the ancestral forest. It's likely that for many centuries, the jagged flows created effective barriers to people, horses, and wild animals. On the south side, what is now named the A G Aiken Lava Bed erupted about 4,000 years ago and is more than four miles long.

On the northern flanks of Mount Adams, far greater in volume and length, are 6,000- to 7,000-year-old andesite flows. The Takh Takh Meadow flow complex is the largest of all Holocene (post-glacial) eruptive units. (A "unit" is determined by age and composition.) Further north is the Muddy Fork lava flow, where magma poured from a mile-long vent stretching from the west side of Red Butte, a basaltic scoria cone, toward the mountain. Although Red Butte looks quite young, it's closer to 14,000 years old. The half-mile-wide cone is the vent for the Trapper Creek basalt flow, which extended eight miles northeastward into the West Fork Klickitat River canyon.

Magnificent Ridge of Wonders dominates the southeast flank of Adams from 8,400 feet down to the forested zone. On the ridge's south side stands 6,821-foot Little Mount Adams, a reddish cinder-spatter cone with a youthful-looking crater. The cone erupted andesite about 60,000 years ago, making it surprisingly older than the bulk of the Mount Adams volcano towering above it. The "Little" one's lavas created a 200-foot-thick bench in the Hellroaring Valley, now occupied by Hellroaring Meadow, Heart Lake, and the cascading waterfalls of Hellroaring Creek.

Roughly eighteen miles in diameter, the broad, forested base of Mount Adams is asymmetrical and elongated toward the south. Arms of lava flows, with vastly different ages, snake out from the edge of the mountain. The longest flow, about 120,000 years old, reaches the 1,400-foot level in the Klickitat Canyon a few miles northeast of the Flying L Ranch. The thick andesite lava forms spectacular columnar cliffs in my favorite part of the canyon near the Skunk Creek overlook. Klickitat Canyon formed an effective lava-flow barrier on the eastern edge of the Mount Adams volcano. The canyon walls are otherwise dominated by Simcoe Mountain basalt, recently dated at about 775,000 years. Above the Glenwood community, a 300,000-year-old dacite flow ends near McCumber Spring, which issues from the flow front and provides the community's water supply.

Darvel provides scale standing at the base of the massive 6,000-year-old Takh Takh Meadow andesite lava flow complex—the largest of Adams' Holocene eruptive units.

The southernmost andesite lava flow is about 56,000 years old and reaches the Trout Lake Valley at the 2,000-foot level. Adjacent and along the edge of the White Salmon River canyon are many more, far older andesite flows, dated at about 457,000 years. Not far to the east are young basalts that originated from Smith Butte only about 14,000 years ago. The northern limit of Mount Adams is a 120,000-year-old andesite flow ending at the 4,000-foot elevation near the base of Green Mountain, beyond

Horseshoe Lake. Close by along the Muddy Fork are andesite lavas that erupted from flank vents about 6,000 years ago. The westernmost lava flow on Mount Adams is 137,000-year-old andesite, which ends at the 2,600-foot level near the Lewis River.

On both sides of the Ridge of Wonders are the oldest lavas on Mount Adams. Radiating dike formations indicate that the eruptive center of the ancestral stratovolcano was about three miles southeast of today's summit. Eruptions began there about 520,000 years ago. Hildreth and Fierstein named the ancestral edifice Hellroaring Volcano. One can only imagine the peak's height and shape, because now only thin air is found above remote and inaccessible glacier basins—the domain of mountain goats. Part of the former northeast flank of the ancestral volcano is exposed as yellowish brecciated rock on Battlement Ridge between the elevations of 8,700 feet and 10,000 feet. But most of its gutted remains are located much lower on the Ridge of Wonders and on the upper parts of Big Muddy and Hellroaring Canyons. By 460,000 years ago, the focus of eruptions appears to have shifted to a location beneath the present-day cone.

Glacial erosion, downcutting by streams, and mass wasting typically wears down the volcanoes faster than they can be built. Mount Adams' total erupted volume of more than 70 cubic miles now amounts to about 48 cubic miles, according Hildreth and Fierstein's estimates. The beautiful U-shaped valleys of Hellroaring Valley and Big Muddy Canyon were carved by the largest glaciers on the mountain during periods of maximum glaciation. This shaping took tens of thousands of years. However, steep headwalls and sharp ridges are evidence of more recently active erosive processes. Erosion can be extremely rapid, even within a human lifetime. I've personally witnessed major changes to more than a few faces on Mount Adams.

The constructive processes that build a volcano eventually stop, but the erosive processes never cease. A million years from now, old Pahto will undoubtedly be extinct and may more closely resemble Goat Rocks—an eroded extinct stratovolcano twenty miles to the north—than its present majestic form. After the volcanic fires have been turned off, once-iconic volcanoes like Mounts Rainier and Adams degrade into just another—though still unique—set of crags, ridges, and glacial-carved valleys.

Top: On both flanks of Ridge of Wonders (upper right) are outcrops of the oldest lavas on Mount Adams, dated at over a half-million years. Little Mount Adams (lower right) erupted andesite about 60,000 years ago.

Left: A breadcrust bomb lies at the northern base of Little Mount Adams.

Chapter 10

Avalanches and Lahars

By forces seemingly antagonistic and destructive, Nature accomplishes her beneficent designs—now a flood of fire, now a flood of ice, now a flood of water; and again in the fullness of time an outburst of organic life. . . .

—John Muir

Draped with early season snow and framed in my living room window, the mountain appeared bright and clear on the morning of October 20, 1997. But something looked different. The Castle and upper part of Battlement Ridge were completely snow-free and had an unnatural brown color. With binoculars, I could see that there had been a huge landslide, but foreground ridges hid most of it from view. I immediately called pilot George Woodruff of Trout Lake. He agreed to fly me and a friend, Harold Cole, to have a look.

As Woodruff's Cessna 172 cleared the Ridge of Wonders, our jaws dropped at the full extent of the dark, reddish brown avalanche deposits covering Klickitat Glacier and reaching well beyond the snout to the 5,600-foot level. The three-mile-long avalanche on the east face of Mount Adams would be the largest in rock volume on Mount Adams in historical times.

I began photographing with my two Nikon film cameras, determined that this amazing event would be well-documented. We looked down on rock and ice blocks as large as three-story houses. I shuddered to think that just two months earlier, I had taken friends from Vermont and Portland across the Klickitat, where the avalanche was now the widest.

We flew eye-level near the huge, oblong scar on the south face of The Castle and upper Battlement Ridge. The scar was about 1,500 feet high between the elevations of about 9,700 feet and 11,200 feet. A year later, after analyzing my before-and-after photos from three different angles, I sketched (to scale) three-dimensional views of

the rocky mass that had broken off.

A second, smaller rock avalanche occurred four days later. The scars of both measured about 1,900 feet long, 800 feet at its maximum width, and 250 feet at the thickest part. I roughly calculated the volume at upwards of six million cubic yards, closely matching the estimate of USGS avalanche expert Dick Iverson, who wrote a short analysis of the slide about a week afterward. The huge mass of falling rock exploded onto the glacier and plowed through icefalls before spreading out more than a half-mile wide.

Seismic stations from central Oregon to northwest Washington recorded the event at twelve-thirty in the morning of October 20, 1997, the same morning of our flight. USGS seismologist Bob Norris, at the University of Washington in Seattle, said the signals lasted about six minutes. He recognized the signals as similar to large rock avalanches on Mount Rainier. Triangulation pointed to the east side of Mount Adams. Norris called me from his office that morning, asking if I'd seen anything unusual on the mountain. But by then, I was already flying over the avalanche with Woodruff and Cole. It was a mind-blowing experience to see the immense transformation of the southeast face.

To say that the Mount Adams Volcano is rotten to the core is not a figure of speech or an exaggeration. Centered beneath the broad summit dome is a mass of over 2.7 *billion* cubic yards of hydrothermally altered rock. That's almost a half of a cubic mile. Alteration of the 1.25-mile-wide fragmental lava core results from thousands of years

On October 20, 1997, the three-mile-long avalanche on Klickitat Glacier was the mountain's largest in rock volume in historical times.

of exposure to sulfur-bearing gases, hot water, and steam. Rising hydrogen sulfide gas from magma becomes oxidized near the surface to form sulfuric acid and elemental sulfur (mined in the 1930s). Over many thousands of years, acid, warm water, and steam reacted chemically with the hard andesite lava, converting it to soft minerals—including kaolinite, alunite, gypsum, and silica. Exposures of the crumbly, multi-colored ("solfatarized") rock are found on the near-vertical cliffs high on the southwest, east, and northwest faces and on the summit cone. Colors range from light gray to hues of yellow, orange, pink, and red. Darvel and I found the stuff easy to pick apart with an ice axe when we climbed the White Salmon Glacier headwall.

Structural collapses of parts of hydrothermally altered volcanic cones typically produce enormous landslides, called debris avalanches. These can transform into lahars (volcanic mudflows), which are rapidly flowing mixtures of water-saturated mud, rock, and other debris. The "other debris" may also include blocks of glacier ice, rafts

of frozen snow, and whole trees. With the consistency of wet concrete, lahars can flow at speeds up to 50 mph and travel tens of miles down rivers that drain the volcano.

Mount Adams may have the largest volume of altered rock of all the stratovolcanoes in the Cascade Range, including Mount Rainier. Shaped somewhat like a bowl, the permeable mass extends downward more than 3,000 feet below the summit cone and *almost 5,000 feet below the surface of White Salmon Glacier* on the southwest face. Three-dimensional mapping of rock alteration and water content was the result of an important 2007 study led by USGS scientist Carol Finn of the Denver office. Airborne magnetic and electromagnetic data was obtained by a helicopter flying a hair-raising, three-mile-square grid pattern over the upper part of the mountain. The chopper skimmed back and forth twenty times or so at an average height of 150 to 200 feet above the icecap, deep crevasses, and vertical cliffs. The distribution of water was mapped for the upper 300 to 700 feet of the volcano, but Finn

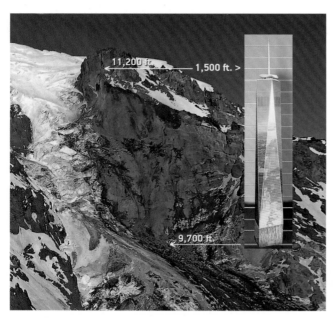

11,200 ft. — 1,500 ft. >

9,700 ft.

Around six million cubic yards of altered rock fell off the upper part of Battlement Ridge and The Castle. The avalanche scar was about 1,500 feet high vertically. New York's Freedom Tower provides scale. *Below:* Crystals of gypsum are embedded in the crumbly, solfatarized rock.

thought it was likely that water-rich rock lay well below the detection depth and could occupy pore space in altered rock at least 3,000 feet below the surface. Finn wrote, "The presence of [pore] water not only helps form clay minerals that weaken the edifice, but also can reduce the effective stress, increasing the potential for slope failure." Rock strength is reduced by up to 85 or 90 percent from alteration, according to a 2002 University of Nevada study.

On Mount Adams, the hazards from lahars exceed all other volcanic dangers, especially in the White Salmon River drainage on the southwest side of the mountain. Jim Vallance, a USGS volcanologist at the Cascades Volcano Observatory (CVO), spent a number of years in the 1980s and early '90s mapping and analyzing four large Holocene (post-Ice Age) lahars in the White Salmon drainage. Vallance's thorough research resulted in a fifty-page booklet published by the USGS in 1999 as Bulletin 2161.

By far the largest lahar in the post-glacial era was the Trout Lake Mudflow, which occurred about 6,000 years ago. An immense mass of hydrothermally altered rock—estimated at around one hundred million cubic yards—broke off the southwest face and rumbled more than thirty-seven miles down the White Salmon River, ending at Husum. What triggered it can only be speculated; possibly a phreatic eruption (steam explosions) or an earthquake. The collapse created a half-mile-wide gap, or cirque, in the summit cone, now occupied by White Salmon Glacier and upper Avalanche Glacier. The resultant lahar buried almost six square miles of the Trout Lake Valley, as much as sixty-five feet deep at its northern edge and tapering to three feet at the south end. Trout Lake (now mostly a marsh) was created when Trout Lake Creek was dammed by the massive mudflow. The valley had been heavily forested at the time, and much of the wood became incorporated in the deposits. Farmers have long since cleared what they could. But some yellowish, clay-rich blocks (called clasts) up to sixteen feet high remain in the fields and near homes and barns. They are mute reminders of the epic event.

About two hundred fifty years ago, the Salt Creek lahar roared down the White Salmon River channel and covered the upper part of Trout Lake Valley to a maximum depth of around thirteen feet. One can see a vertically exposed section of it from the Martin Road bridge, where

My wife Nancy seems miniaturized in the midst of huge rocks and rubble at 7,800 feet on Klickitat Glacier, just one year after the historic 1997 avalanche. The boulder next to her is the size of a three-story house.

it crosses the White Salmon River. Along the banks of the river are buried logs and pieces of mineralized rock from the summit cone of Mount Adams.

Tom Pierson, a USGS hydrologist specializing in lahars at the Cascades Volcano Observatory, estimated that the Salt Creek lahar occurred between 1758 and 1762. This age estimate is based on tree-ring dating that Pierson and I did in 2014. We cored the oldest Douglas firs on the lahar terrace at about the 3,400-foot level in the Cascade Creek Valley. Pierson made his estimate after counting the rings of the oldest tree and making adjustments for the height of the tree core sample, lag time required for tree seedlings to sprout and grow upon the lahar deposit, and other factors.

The lahar began as a landslide of severely altered rock at about 12,000 feet on the west-facing cliffs above Avalanche Glacier. Vallance estimated the mass of altered rock that broke off at 20 to 25 million cubic yards. The volume equivalent might be visualized as a rectangular slab about a half-mile long, 1,000 feet wide, and 250 feet thick. The evidence today is a concave source area of roughly those dimensions on the near vertical headwall of Avalanche Glacier. Visible from many miles away are yellowish slide and lahar deposits covering a broad swath of the mountain below the glacier. A deeper blanket of the same material covers the lower part of Avalanche Glacier—preserving ice that formed during the Little Ice Age, which lasted until the mid-1800s.

On foot, Vallance followed and studied the path of the Salt Creek lahar to the Trout Lake Valley. At the confluence of Salt and Cascade creeks (3,100-foot level) the flow's depth was about seventy feet. Moving as fast as 45 mph, it ran up the opposite valley slope an additional seventy feet. Several miles down valley, where the White Salmon River enters the narrows, solfatarized rocks were deposited on benches as high as 180 feet above the river level.

The half-mile-wide White Salmon Glacier amphitheater was created about 6,000 years ago, when roughly one hundred million cubic yards of hydrothermally altered rock broke off and became the Trout Lake Mudflow. *Below:* A large clast near a home in the Trout Lake Valley is a mute reminder of the event. The Trout Lake Mudflow, a lahar, buried almost six square miles of the valley up to sixty-five feet deep.

Vallance wrote that lahars of that size are "rare, and the probability of their occurrence . . . is difficult to evaluate." In 2017, a USGS web page titled "Hazards of Mount Adams" predicted "the annual probability of a future lahar large enough to affect the Trout Lake area . . . is estimated to be 0.1 to 1 percent," meaning that during any given year, the odds of a big lahar would be from one-in-a-thousand to one-in-a-hundred. However, a 2010 Oregon State University study suggests that the risk of a mega subduction earthquake on the northern segment of the Cascadia fault is around 10 to 15 percent in the next fifty years. We know that major earthquakes in other parts of the world have generated huge debris avalanches, although the last major subduction zone earthquake on January 26, 1700, which swamped major sections of the Washington / Oregon coast, did not cause a significant lahar on Mount Adams.

Left: The yellowish deposits at right-center are from a large debris avalanche about 250 years ago, which then quickly transformed into the Salt Creek lahar. *Right:* The Salt Creek lahar covers the upper Trout Lake Valley to a maximum depth of about thirteen feet.

The actual probability of a large lahar on the mountain in the near term is very hard to call. A 1995 USGS Mount Adams Hazards report stated that lahars " . . . may be triggered by magma intrusions, steam explosions, earthquakes or intense rainstorms. But others [called unheralded lahars] have no apparent trigger and may result from gradual weakening of rock masses that finally become unstable enough to fail." Without additional evidence, unheralded failure of weakened rock probably is the best explanation for the Salt Creek lahar two hundred fifty years ago.

In his 1999 study, Vallance recommended acquisition of a lahar-warning-and-detection system for the Trout Lake Valley. I began my own mission to bring the lahar hazard issue into the public spotlight in November 2001 with a "Mount Adams Volcano" slide show at the Trout Lake School. The gymnasium was packed with about three hundred fifty people.

Thirteen years went by with little progress, except for the word getting out. In 2014, I joined Rachel Haymon, a marine geologist with a seasonal home in Trout Lake, to form a citizens group called LEAP—Lahar Event Awareness and Preparation. Our USGS liaison and advisor is Tom Pierson, who lives in the Glenwood Valley. Haymon stimulated renewed interest through special public meetings with the Trout Lake Community Council, and began to seek means of developing a lahar detection-and-warning system. Pierson and I gave informational slide shows. The Trout Lake Community Council, led by Tim Webster, supported the efforts of LEAP and began working on an emergency plan for the Trout Lake community. The long-range goal of the USGS is to establish lahar detection-and-warning systems for communities at risk below volcanoes in the Cascade chain. This worthy goal, however, is a long way from congressional funding. Even if Congress eventually approved the funds, it could be many years before the USGS would actually install a working warning system for the White Salmon River Valley.

The USGS Cascades Volcano Observatory uses Acoustic Flow Monitors (AFMs) to detect lahars originating on Mount St. Helens, and in the Carbon and Puyallup valleys of Mount Rainier. The Mount Rainier system cost a million dollars, and Pierce County spends about thirty thousand dollars a year to maintain the monitors. However, the design of that system requires more time for a warning to be delivered than is available to Trout Lake, which is much closer to the mountain.

To accomplish this, Rachel Haymon teamed up with her colleague Robin Matoza at University of California

Top: At the edge of the upper valley, the White Salmon River is still in the process of eroding through the 250-year-old lahar deposits. *Above:* In 2014, USGS hydrologist Tom Pierson cores a Douglas fir to date the Salt Creek lahar using tree rings. Tom estimates that it occurred between 1758 and 1762.

(Santa Barbara) to detect and study mass-wasting events on Mount Adams using an acoustic sensor array. Lahars and debris avalanches produce infrasound signals, or low-frequency sounds below the threshold of human hearing. At this writing, a pilot study of background infrasound signals may show whether or not such a detection system will work. If it does, then collaboration can begin with Klickitat County to incorporate the same method of lahar detection, which can be operated via the county's 24/7 emergency dispatch center and reverse-911 system.

A USGS computer model to predict lahar inundation limits can now estimate what areas in any particular river valley or canyon would be affected by lahars of different volumes. Maps showing potential inundation areas in the White Salmon River Valley provide some adjustment to the hazard zones depicted in the 1995 hazard assessment for Mount Adams. Older reports and USGS maps of volcanic hazards on Mount Adams are available in print and online.

Tom Pierson of the USGS offered advice for residents of river valleys downstream of active volcanoes (up to one hundred miles away), or those who spend time recreating on their flanks. Hikers on Mounts Adams, Hood, St. Helens, Rainier, Baker, Glacier Peak, Shasta, and other large volcanoes should learn to recognize these signs of possible lahar danger:

- A distant low booming sound (and, possibly, a dark dust cloud if the summit area is visible) caused by a large mass of collapsing, avalanching rock.
- A persistent low-frequency rumbling sound that slowly gets progressively louder (like an approaching freight train).
- The sudden change of clear river water to very muddy, particularly if the water appears to be thickening with mud, changing its viscosity, and starting to roll boulders in the flow.
- Sharp cracks of breaking trees or the sight of vegetation violently shaking or falling a relatively short distance upstream.
- A strong earthquake, a volcanic explosion (if the volcano is in a state of unrest), or exceptionally prolonged and intense rainfall, any of which could trigger a lahar.

A 2017 repeat photo of Mount Adams' southwest face from Crofton Ridge reveals the regeneration of trees since 1901. The 1760 lahar covered almost the entire area below the moraines. (Top: Harry F. Reid, NSIDC)

The Great Slide of 1921 knocked down many trees at the subalpine level on the southwest flank. It was a huge avalanche—a thousand acres in size—of mostly snow and ice, draped by a thin deposit of pulverized rock.

If hikers see or hear any of these signs, they are advised to seek high ground—at least one hundred feet above the valley floor—as quickly as possible. In the upper White Salmon River Valley, there is little time to waste. A large lahar could reach the town of Trout Lake in about twenty minutes.

A comforting bit of reality is this: Avalanches of rock, mud, ice, and snow do not turn into lahars if they are not fully saturated with water. Without saturation, they typically do not flow as far as lahars of the same volume. Many such rock-ice avalanches (called mixed avalanches) have occurred on Mount Adams since the retreat of Ice Age glaciers about eleven thousand years ago (the Holocene era). Avalanche deposits of that era extend as far as five miles from the summit on nearly every flank of the mountain.

The "Great Slide of 1921" was the first mixed avalanche to receive wide publicity in the Pacific Northwest. Darvel and I had often speculated about its location below timberline, having hiked the area for many years. More

than thirty years ago, Jim Vallance stopped by my home in Glenwood and sketched the extent of the Great Slide. The avalanche originated at about 12,000 feet on the same rotten, west-facing headwall above Avalanche Glacier as had the Salt Creek lahar.

Of the four lobes that extended below timberline, the longest ended near the 5,000-foot level in the Salt Creek Valley. In the 1921 edition of *Mazama*, Frank Byam wrote, "Whole forests were broken down or uprooted, and the trees ground to bits. Level places became hills. Canyons were filled with debris of all kinds, and the whole face of the mountain was changed."

I found photos in Art Jones's album, along with two others published in the journal *Mazama*, that clearly show an avalanche of mostly snow and ice, draped by thin deposits of pulverized rock. That might explain the difference in area estimates: "five or six thousand acres" noted in the earlier *Mazama* article, as opposed to Vallance's estimate of about a thousand acres. The thin deposits shown

This image beautifully captures "The Great Slide of 1921" not long after it occurred. (Fred Kiser, Mazamas Collection)

in 1921 photos, covering a much larger area, would have disappeared after a few years of rainfall and erosion. Most of the small, downed trees would also be gone years later, leaving little or no evidence of the avalanche.

The 1921 avalanche occurred in May, after an exceptionally wet winter and spring. High pore-water content could have triggered the failure of heavily altered rock on the Avalanche Glacier headwall. A small steam explosion also might have caused the collapse. Climbers in 1924 reported a group of steam vents less than a thousand feet below the cliffs. A year or two later, vent activity died out.

There seems to be no evidence or reports of large rock-and-ice avalanches on Mount Adams between 1921 and 1982. However, during the summers of 1983, 1997, 2008, and 2012, mixed avalanches two to three miles long swept down Avalanche Glacier, creating scars easily visible from Portland. The slides on the southwest face were very similar, but smaller than the Great Slide of 1921. All four originated from the same headwall above Avalanche

Glacier. Most of the glacier had been destroyed in each avalanche, and the rock content was very low in volume compared to the amount of snow and ice.

In 2017, the Pacific Northwest Seismic Network (PNSN) included only one outdated seismometer on Mount Adams. It was designated "ASR" and located at 4,400 hundred feet on Stagman Ridge on the southwest flank, about six miles from the source area of the largest mixed avalanches on Avalanche Glacier headwall.

As a keen observer of anything unusual on Mount Adams, I have photographed the scars and deposits of the five big avalanches on the mountain since 1983, shortly after they occurred. And for other significant events on Mount Adams over the years, I wrote articles and sent out illustrated reports to many people. The crumbly face of the mountain is changing almost from year to year, but only to a perceptive viewer. In geologic terms, the rate of change is extremely rapid. I am humbled that I've been able to play a small role in recording this amazing process.

Chapter 11

Shrinking Glaciers

The study of glaciers is a fascinating one. They are the greatest of all landscape-makers; and mighty is their influence in shaping the destiny of continents.

— C. E. Rusk

Many years ago, I acquired a large number of high-resolution glacier photos taken on Mount Adams in August 1901. Professor Harry F. Reid of Johns Hopkins University was the photographer. I returned to a number of the glaciers to obtain precise then-and-now views from the same sites. Repeat photography is extremely helpful in comparing thickness and extent of glaciers over a span of time. (Even more accomplished at this kind of work is Hassan Basagic, a friend associated with Portland State University.)

I'm especially interested in the loss of glacier *volume*, but no scientific estimates have yet been made on Mount Adams. On Mount Rainier, however, Park Geologist Scott Beason estimated glacier volume loss since 1896 at more than 50 percent. Between 2008 and 2015, the rate of volume loss increased dramatically: about five times higher than the overall rate since 1913.

The two lobes of Lyman Glacier on Mount Adams' northeast face are fed directly by the summit icecap. Based on my repeat photo of the glacier in 2013, the vigorous icefalls of Lyman appear about 150 feet thinner than they were in 1901; the icefalls may now be only about 100 feet (or less) thick. About a mile below the present Lyman Glacier terminus, between lateral moraines is a 300-foot-deep rocky basin bisected by a rushing glacial stream. In 1901 the same basin was filled with ice.

Mazama Glacier was an impressive glacier in 1901. Repeat photos reveal astounding changes in thickness and area. The PSU study shows Mazama Glacier lost almost half of its area in the past hundred-plus years. I estimate the glacier lost *two-thirds or more* volume during the same period.

Other glaciers have similar or greater volume loss, in my opinion. Lava Glacier on the north side now occupies only a *quarter* of the area that it did at the turn of the twentieth century. Rusk's 1919 photo of Lava Glacier from high on Lava Ridge resembles an alpine glacier in Alaska. It's now a vast, rocky plain vegetated with arctic willows, mountain sorrel, and other hardy plants.

Adams Glacier, largest on the mountain, lost about a mile in length during the past century. It now ends on a gentle slope at about 7,100 feet, nearly three miles from its source near the mountain's summit. Far beyond and wider than its withering terminus is an amazing array of lateral moraines, dating to the Little Ice Age. The sharp moraines vividly show that a great ice sheet with multiple lobes existed just a few hundred years ago.

In North America, the Little Ice Age occurred roughly between 700 and 150 years ago. Glaciers around the world reached their maximum growth since the end of the Pleistocene (Ice Age). Little Ice Age (or "Neoglacial") moraines mark the former thickness, width, and length of glaciers. Many are massive ridges of loose rock. The tallest moraine on Mount Adams is located below Gotchen Glacier, ironically now the smallest glacier on the mountain.

By the end of the Little Ice Age in the mid-1800s, nearly all glaciers in the Cascades were in retreat. Nisqually Glacier on Mount Rainier began its recession around 1840, based on botanical evidence. C. E. Rusk was likely the first to make note of glacier shrinkage on Mount Adams. He observed Klickitat Glacier receding nearly a quarter-mile between 1890 and 1919. When he guided Professor Harry

Repeat photography of Wilson, Lyman, and Lava glaciers in 2013 and 1901 reveals their dramatic decrease in thickness during the past century. (Top: Harry F. Reid, NSIDC)

A Portland State University study in 2006 shows that Mazama Glacier lost almost half of its area since the turn of the twentieth century. Actual ice *volume* loss since 1901 could be two-thirds or more. (Top: William R. King, Darryl Lloyd Collection)

Beyond the withering terminus of Adams Glacier is an array of Little Ice Age moraines, where a broad ice sheet had branched into multiple tongues.

F. Reid around Mount Adams in 1901, glaciers covered more than twelve square miles of the mountain—about twice the area covered today.

Stories of smaller glaciers in Oregon "vanishing" made newspaper headlines in the 1930s. Yet in the mid-1940s, the century-long climatic warming and glacier recession reversed itself in the Pacific Northwest, marking the beginning of a three-decade period of cooler temperatures and greater snowfall. Glaciers on Mount Adams and other Cascade peaks responded by thickening, and even advancing, during this relatively brief period.

By the early 1980s, sharp increases in average temperatures in the Cascades (and globally) had renewed the pattern of glacier shrinkage and retreat on Mount Adams. A thin layer of Mount St. Helens ash from the 1980 eruption also contributed significantly to the loss of permanent snow and ice during the long melt seasons of the 1980s. The dark, thin layer of ash on glaciers and snowfields resulted in much greater absorption of solar radiation.

It's too bad that a pattern of snow stakes wasn't placed into drill holes on at least one Mount Adams glacier during the early 1980s. The rate of ablation (most of which is meltwater) could have been measured, and mass balances could have been tracked, for at least a few years to determine the rate and amount of glacier-volume loss.

Glacier shrinkage accelerated in the mid-1990s and continued at least through 2015. Working under glaciologist and professor Andrew Fountain, a 2006 study by Danielle Sitts and Matthew Hoffman at Portland State University revealed that the total area covered by the twelve glaciers on Mount Adams decreased by almost 50 percent between 1904 and 2006. More than 12 square miles of glaciated area had shrunk to about 6.25 square miles during the century. Summer air temperature was the main factor in glacial retreat, as total precipitation figures showed little change over the past century. According to the PSU study, the overall summer air temperature on Mount Adams in the second half of the century was warmer by about 2.7°F than it was during the first half of the 1900s.

In the Cascades, warming temperatures resulted in rising snowlines, decreasing mountain snowpack, and an earlier spring runoff. The Climate Impacts Group at University of Washington projected a much more rapid increase in the warming rate—in the range of

The Lava Glacier headwall was almost completely bare of ice in 2007. The Portland State University team found that the glacier occupied only a quarter of the area that it had in 1901. (Inset: Harry F. Reid, NSIDC)

plus-6°F—during the first half of the twenty-first century, compared to the last half of the twentieth century.

Before about 1980, permanent snow and ice on glacier headwalls cemented rubbly layers of lava in place. This was especially true on Mazama, Pinnacle, Adams, and Lava glaciers; but with climate warming, headwalls have become increasingly bare. Strong winds raise clouds of dust that drift downwind to settle on snowfields and glaciers already darkened to an unknown extent by atmospheric soot. Glacier and snowfield melting then accelerates due to the increased absorption of solar radiation. Ongoing research on the influence of soot on Mount Adams may soon reveal quantifiable data.

Mount Adams appeared dazzling white in May 2009, as it typically appears each spring. But by late fall of that year, its glaciers—and even the icecap—were as dark and dirty as I had ever seen them in my life. From the International Space Station, on October 11, 2009, National Aeronautics and Space Administration (NASA) astronauts photographed Mount Adams two hundred miles or so directly below them. Their historic photo showed White Salmon Glacier almost completely camouflaged by brown dust. The mountain's other diminished glaciers, all bare ice with no snow cover by this late date, were barely distinguishable.

Dust and debris will have an insulating effect if the layer becomes more than about an inch thick, according to Professor Fountain. Rockfalls from glacier headwalls have become more frequent, especially during the spring and summer seasons. By late summer, thick rock deposits cover most of the area of at least three glaciers: Pinnacle, Lava, and Avalanche. All three may become "debris-covered glaciers" within the coming decades. Over the years, I've identified about a half-dozen unnamed debris-covered glaciers on all sides of Mount Adams. Fountain explained that true "rock glaciers" are moving piles of rocks with ice in the voids.

In 2013, Hugh McMahan and I located the exact spot that Harry F. Reid stood in 1901 to photograph Adams Glacier, the largest of twelve on the mountain. (Top: Harry F. Reid, NSIDC)

Insulation by rocky material on the lower sections of Rusk and Klickitat glaciers has reduced ice melt, and even allowed their snouts to remain in nearly the same positions over the past two decades or so. Klickitat Glacier descends to 5,700 feet, more than two miles into the canyon of Big Muddy Creek. The huge rock avalanche of October 1997 added about five million cubic yards of rock debris to the glacier's lower half. During the same period, however, overall ice wastage and dramatic thinning of the two glaciers has continued unabated.

Mount Adams' largest glaciers—Adams, Lyman, Klickitat, Rusk, and Wilson—are the healthiest because the mile-wide summit icecap feeds them both directly by ice flow and indirectly by ice avalanches. Fountain predicts that few, if any, large glaciers will exist in the contiguous United States by the end of this century. A glacier has to be perennial ice or snow that moves, and many glaciers today will become stagnant ice patches or snowfields. Depending on the slope angle, compacted snow and ice doesn't flow as a glacier if the thickness is less than about sixty-five feet (twenty meters), and the icecaps of Mount Adams and Mount Rainier are too small to keep up with overall glacial melting.

The scientific evidence is clear: "Global change caused by human activities is occurring now," according to the American Association for the Advancement of Science and the world's scientific societies. At the end of 2016, bad news got even worse for Planet Earth. It was the third successive year for the highest-ever average surface temperatures since records began in 1880. The year 2017 ranked second-warmest, and in January 2018, NASA reported that Earth's average surface temperature was almost 2°F (a little more than 1°C) above the pre-industrial-era benchmark. United Nations climate negotiators had agreed to capping global warming at "well below" 3.6°F (2°C) by the end of the century, but recent research points to only a 5 percent chance of that happening.

In early November 2006, an "atmospheric river" of subtropical tropical moisture brought record-breaking rainfall to the central part of the Cascade Range. During a three-day period from November 5 to 7, Laurel Mountain in the Coast Range of Oregon received almost 50 inches, which is 12 inches more than the previous record. Lee's Camp in Tillamook County received 14.3 inches in a single day, the wettest day in Oregon's recorded history. On Mount Rainier, 18 inches of rain fell in thirty-six hours during the 2006 storm. On Mount Hood, freezing levels rose to 10,000 feet and 13 inches fell during the same period. Jim Vallance of the USGS estimated between 10 and 20 inches on Mount Adams when there was very little winter snow to absorb, like a sponge, such phenomenal and relentless rainfall.

Unleashed were the greatest debris flows in recorded history on Mounts Adams, Hood, St. Helens, and Rainier.

No one knows the science of debris flows better than Dick Iverson, senior research hydrologist at the USGS Cascade Volcano Observatory. Iverson defines debris flows as "water-laden masses of soil and fragmented rock that rush down mountainsides, funnel into stream channels, entrain objects in their paths, and form lobate deposits when they spill onto valley floors." Fortunately the November 2006 storm did not result in destruction of roads, bridges, or facilities on Mount Adams, such as occurred on the other three volcanoes. But the debris-flow events began when steep lateral moraines and glacial till in six glacier basins became waterlogged, and huge sections collapsed while being undercut by boulder-clogged torrents.

Perhaps the biggest of the seven Mount Adams 2006 debris flows originated on Avalanche Glacier on the southwest face. A surface flow on the glacier surface broke through 200- to 300-year-old ice at a breach in the lateral moraine at 7,400 feet, producing a 200-foot-high vertical wall of unconsolidated rock. Below it, a grinding, pounding, and deafening mass of saturated rock carved a channel (or chasm, actually) more than 100 feet deep for about a mile through the thinly forested slope. The violent debris flow reached the 6,000-foot level, and then roared several miles down the steep Salt Creek ravine before depositing a vast boulder plain below the mouth of the canyon at around 3,700 feet. The event ended with a mudflow into the Cascade Creek marsh at 3,340 feet. It raised the water level about three feet, ultimately killing hundreds of hardwoods.

The Adams Creek event of 2006 resulted in another massive boulder plain about a quarter-mile wide and tens of feet thick in the subalpine area around 6,000 feet. Adams Creek's new channel at the Pacific Crest Trail (PCT) crossing is now about a quarter-mile northwest of where it once flowed. On the east side of Mount Adams, debris flows down the Big Muddy and Rusk Creek did not originate from lateral moraines. Instead, multiple erosion channels were carved in glacial till and avalanche deposits south of the Klickitat Glacier terminus and below Rusk Glacier. The north branch of Rusk Creek flows down a vertical-sided gulch, first carved by debris flows in 1988 from glacial outburst floods. The debris flow of November 2006 deepened the 1988 channel considerably. Rusk Creek flows into Big Muddy Creek at the 4,400-foot level, and

The difference in the Klickitat icefalls between 1969 and 1998 is apparent. Besides loss due to climate warming, the glacier suffered a large loss of volume in the rock avalanche of 1997.

enormous rock deposits from the combined debris flows cover forested areas in Big Muddy Creek canyon floor down to at least the 4,000-foot level.

In summary, the source of the flows is over-steepened moraines left by the retreating glaciers. These moraines are unstable and subject to failure. Studies show that with climate change, extreme precipitation and flooding events are greater in magnitude and increasingly more destructive. More large debris flow events are inevitable in Mount Adams' future, and the next flows may be far more damaging to trails, roads, bridges, and irrigation diversion structures.

Looking down on the top of The Castle in 1934 and 2003, dramatic changes are apparent at the edge of The Castle and Battlement Ridge, as well as length and width of Klickitat Glacier. (*Top:* Dick Mansfield Collection)

Left: Ash from Mount St. Helens' 1980 eruption darkened the glaciers and snowfields of Mount Adams. As a result, melting was greater than normal by September that year. (Mazamas Collection) *Right:* On October 11, 2009, an astronaut's photo of Mount Adams from the International Space Station reveals all of the glaciers as amazingly dirty and diminished in size. (NASA)

More than one hundred feet deep, the chasm of upper Salt Creek was eroded by a huge debris flow on November 6 and 7, 2006, after ten to twenty inches of rain fell on Avalanche Glacier and elsewhere on the mountain.

The violent debris flow roared several miles down the steep Salt Creek channel before depositing a vast boulder plain below the mouth of the canyon.

Chapter 12

Wildfires and Forests

Fire epitomizes change and transformation, the unpredictable and uncontrollable essence of nature. Fire is wildness in motion . . . the essential rhythm-keeper, the percussive element that sets the beat for the movement of life.

— Mollie Matteson

Returning from a Mount Adams hike in August 2015, a friend and I talked about how the area along upper Bird Creek Road was long overdue for a big fire. The trees were all small and even-aged, and I mentioned that the forest we were passing through last burned in 1885. We watched a weak thunderstorm drift from the Hood River Valley northward toward Klickitat and Yakima counties of Washington. There were a few lightning strikes off in the distance and accompanied by a little rain, but activity was nothing like some storms. Near the end of the afternoon, one lone strike hit a tree at about the 4,700-foot level on Mount Adams, just inside Tract D of the Yakama Reservation. The spot was in a heavily logged area of pine and fir near Cougar Creek and Cress Camp, an old sheepherder's camp. Extreme drought and record-low snowpack made the forest tinder dry with very little moisture in the soil. We saw the flash and heard the rumble from inside my car.

The struck tree ignited and would be the origin of the great Cougar Creek Fire of 2015. The blaze would burn for a month across 53,500 acres—nearly 84 square miles—and extend from the south side of the mountain around to the northeast side. Fighting it with 444 personnel would cost more than twenty-five million dollars. It would be, by far, the largest wildfire in recorded history on Mount Adams.

At six o'clock in the morning of August 11, following our Bird Creek Meadows hike and lightning strike, I heard through Darlisa Black's online grapevine that a fire about a hundred acres in size was burning in timber about six miles above the Glenwood Valley. It had spread south overnight into Washington Department of Natural Resources land, and a DNR bulldozer had been sent up to clear a firebreak. Soon afterward the operator had no choice but to retreat. By early afternoon the fire had expanded to about 1,500 acres. Low-humidity, easterly winds were spreading the blaze rapidly westward. I drove to the edge of Camas Prairie and photographed the towering pyrocumulus cloud and billowing smoke that completely obscured Mount Adams.

That same morning, Yakama Nation Recreation Area Ranger Richard Canapoo and his assistant were urgently evacuating campgrounds and hikers in the Bird Lake–Bench Lake area. By afternoon, everyone had cleared the area. It was a praiseworthy effort, and Richard could do little else but evacuate as quickly as possible. He had no time to pull out the Yakama Nation trailers at Mirror and Bird lakes, off-road vehicles, and other equipment, such as a wood-splitter. The fire was moving much too rapidly toward the Bird Creek Road, the only escape route out of the Recreation Area.

In the meantime, a large volunteer team of horseback riders was organized to round up about a thousand head of cattle owned by the Neil Kayser family of Goldendale. The cattle grazed on allotments covering the southeastern slopes of the mountain between Glenwood Valley and the 5,600-foot level. (More than thirty cows plus calves would be lost in the fire.)

The fire raged during the night in strong easterly winds. By seven o'clock on the morning of August 12, it had expanded to about 6,000 acres, reaching the Gifford Pinchot National Forest boundary. By eleven that morning, it had grown to 9,400 acres, and during the day, dense smoke plumes and an enormous pyrocumulus cloud filled the northern part of the sky. The smoke seemed to envelop Mount Adams when I photographed it from Hood River. The mountain's upper slopes, however, were actually in the clear behind the plumes, and Lucas King of Trout Lake captured dramatic photos of the spreading fire from Adams' summit.

The blaze nearly doubled in size to 18,000 acres during a twelve-hour period between noon and midnight on August 12. In just two days with low humidity and east winds, it had equaled the size of "The Great Conflagration of 1885," which had burned three-quarters of Section 17 on the south and southeast sides of Mount Adams.

On the morning of August 13, 2015, the fire had spread over Mirror Lake and Bird Lake, and reached the edges of Bird Creek Meadows. Expansion was especially rapid toward the west. After jumping the A G Aiken Lava Bed, it re-burned all of the 2008 Cold Springs Fire area of nearly 8,000 acres—a portion of it for the third time (the second had been in 2012).

Between three hundred and five hundred firefighters headed to Glenwood, while division superintendents and strike teams of engines were out scouting and developing strategy. The historic Gotchen Creek Guard Station, built in 1909, was wrapped in fire-resistant foil and sprinklers were installed. The fire burned about two hundred fifty feet from the cabin, but fortunately never reached it. Only aerial firefighting had been used so far.

By midday on August 14, the wind direction changed and the blaze headed toward the northeast and east. After crossing Hellroaring Creek, it spread across The Island and beyond Big Muddy Creek. In the weeks that followed, nearly all of the fire growth was in the closed part of the Yakama Reservation. The Incident Command Center was at the Glenwood School, and residents of the valley went all-out to support the huge firefighting effort, much of which was concentrated on keeping the fire from reaching homes at the edge of the valley. (The closest it got to Glenwood was about five miles.) Firefighting in the closed part of the reservation consisted mainly of huge burnouts—documented in dramatic photos by

On August 11, 2015, the lightning-caused Cougar Creek Fire was in its second day and expanding rapidly toward the west. Pyrocumulus clouds tower over Mount Adams in this view from Camas Prairie.

A month after the 84-square-mile Cougar Creek Fire ended, an aerial view toward the east shows the boundary between the Yakama Reservation, left, and Washington Department of Natural Resources land, right.

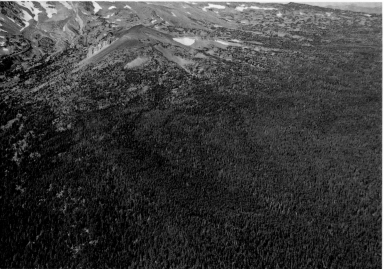

Between 2006 (top) and 2011, an infestation of mountain pine beetles killed the lodgepole pine on the east side, turning the forest a rust color.

two hundred wildfires across Eastern Washington.) By the second week in October 2012, the Mount Adams fire had burned about thirty-one square miles of national forest, and cost more than fifteen million dollars to fight. It extended from the A G Aiken Lava Bed on the south side of the mountain, around to Riley Creek on the west side, reaching as high as 7,400 feet near the South Climb Trail and as low as 3,900 feet in the Cascade Creek Valley. The fire covered about 40 percent of the forested part of the wilderness, and impacted twenty-eight miles of trails, including the PCT and Round-the-Mountain Trail.

I spent most of September 9, 2012, photographing the blaze as it spread eastward in strong winds. By early afternoon, the smoke plume mushroomed possibly 20,000 feet into the sky, and I knew from my aerial surveys and past hikes that it had hit the insect-damaged forest of the Morrison Creek basin. About 65 percent of the Cascade Creek Fire was stand-replacement, and the fire burned at highest intensity where insect damage was worst.

To some extent, this was true for the far bigger Cougar Creek Fire of 2015. Prior to both fires, mortality was very heavy in lodgepole pine infested with mountain pine beetle. There had also been defoliation of true firs by western balsam bark beetle, balsam woolly adelgid, and spruce budworm in an outbreak that peaked in the late 1990s.

Each time I fly around Mount Adams in a chartered plane, normally on an annual basis, I take hundreds of photographs. The comparison between 2006 and 2011 montane forest photos is amazing. In the stretch of five years, a whole forest of green lodgepole pine on the east side of the mountain had died and turned rust-colored.

Fire suppression during the past century caused significant overcrowding in the forests, and combined with climate warming, trees had become severely stressed. Widespread mortality by beetles resulted when unhealthy trees were unable to resist the insects. Pitch production in lodgepole pine was insufficient to kill the beetles or expel them through the pitch tubes.

While hiking through such a damaged forest, Darvel and I would often bring up the sixty-four-thousand-dollar question of *when* it would burn, not *if*. We would try to imagine a firestorm on Mount Adams, if all the right atmospheric conditions were met. So on August 13, 2015, I watched with fascination and apprehension the monstrous

my neighbor Jurgen Hess—along major logging roads. Strong rainstorms arrived in mid-September to make short order of the containment mission. Almost 80 percent of the fire occurred in the Yakama Reservation, and more than half of that area burned at moderate to high severity, or "stand-replacement" (meaning most trees are killed).

Just three years earlier, in September 2012, lightning started the Cascade Creek Fire on Crofton Ridge in the Mount Adams Wilderness of Gifford Pinchot National Forest. (The same lightning storm started more than

In the late 1980s, *Bacillus thuringiensis*, or Bt, insecticide was sprayed on Mount Adams' eastside forests to control the outbreak of spruce budworm, which peaked about ten years later.

smoke plume of the Cougar Creek Fire. I thought there was no way the conflagration could ever be stopped by humans. And were it not for the mid-September rainstorms, a far greater portion of the Yakama Reservation, and even the national forest, could have been enveloped by fire.

According to a 2016 study by researchers at the University of Idaho and Columbia University, more than several decades of human-caused climate change had played a "resounding role" in causing wildfires in the western states to burn hotter, faster, and nearly twice as large.

The Google Earth time-lapse comparison of midsummer Mount Adams' forests between 1985 and 2016 is startling. No single image can tell the story better. Only about a third (or less) of the montane forested belt on the mountain remained unburned in 2016 and at this writing in 2018. Young trees occupy most of the still-forested area.

Darvel and I have hiked extensively in the burned forests of Adams and Hood, especially since 2009. Seeing the transformed land through successive years after fires occur is a real learning experience. We've seen how plant regeneration goes into full swing during the first growing season following the fires. Even in the most severe burns on Adams, plants like beargrass and corn lily spurt

Deadfall of lodgepole pine in the eastside forest one year before the 2015 Cougar Creek Fire. *Below:* Lightning also started the 31-square-mile Cascade Creek Fire in late summer 2012. Photographing it from the west, I knew that it had hit the Morrison Creek basin with its heavy tree mortality from insects and pathogens.

upward through the charred soil. Scattered around are untouched meadows and patches of green conifers. In October 2016, we hiked with friends through a year-old burn on the west side of Mount Adams. At about the 5,200-foot level, we watched a small flock of black-backed woodpeckers feed on the larvae of wood beetles in the blackened silver fir snags.

"Severely burned forests are neither destroyed nor lifeless," wrote Dr. Richard Hutto, Professor of Biology at the University of Montana. "They are essential for maintaining an important part of the biological diversity we value today."

Three years after the Cold Springs Fire, in 2011, we marveled at the return of new growth and life near the A G Aiken Lava Bed. I photographed a snag-filled wetland that was lush with red monkeyflowers, yellow arnica, and many species of green plants. Up the trail were hundreds of small aspen saplings; their parent trees had been incinerated. Glorious displays of blooming beargrass blanketed higher parts of the 2008 burn. The area re-burned in 2015, probably reversing the earlier recovery and wiping out most of the dead snags.

An event like the 2015 burn could create a wetland meadow in that area. One of the distinctive aspects of the middle-elevation forested belt around Mount Adams is the diversity of meadow types. Fire probably played a major role in creating large open areas, such as Muddy Meadows on the north side and Grand Meadows on the west side. Fire destroys and transforms. It is as much a part of the landscape as the trees themselves. Our good friend Christine Colasurdo hiked through scorched dead firs in Oregon to find a huge patch of pink bleeding hearts.

In October 2016, a year after the 2015 Horseshoe Fire on the west side of Adams, we watched black-backed woodpeckers feed on the larvae of wood beetles in silver fir snags. (Inset: USFWS)

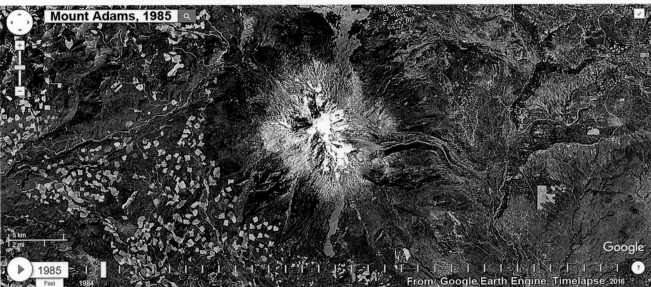

A 1985–2016 time-lapse comparison of midsummer Mount Adams' forests tells a graphic story. Only about a third of the montane forested belt remained unburned in 2016. (Google Earth)

"Forests and flowers. Sometimes they are intertwined, like fungi and rain," she said. "Fire is a moment for the forest. Then the forest evolves and, along with it, our perceptions of fire."

Botanists David Biek and Susan McDougall wrote in 2007 that the mountain is home to eighteen conifer species. The rarest trees they found were Sitka spruce and western yew. The wide diversity of conifer species can be attributed to a number of factors, including Mount Adams' location east of the Cascade Crest, the mountain's topography, soils,

moisture, and the many different forested zones, ranging from the 2,000-foot level to tree line. But wildfires over the millennia have also played a major role.

Old-growth trees (at least several hundred years old) remaining on Mount Adams are few and far between, largely because of wildfires and logging on the lower slopes. However, two old-growth tree species are found at the subalpine level. The first are the gnarliest and oldest living whitebark pines around timberline—trees that resisted blister rust fungus and beetles. The second are

A parkland of stately old-growth ponderosa pines characterize the lower southeastern flanks of Mount Adams during the late 1940s and early 1950s. (Judith Harvey Collection)

Three years after the 2008 Cascade Creek Fire, lush wildflowers bloom near a spring at the edge of the A G Aiken Lava Bed.

two isolated stands of large, often-unnoticed mountain hemlock, located near 6,000 feet on the western flanks, and on the southeast side below Bird Creek Meadows, near Hellroaring Ridge. They also managed to survive fires, insects, disease, animal disruption, and human cuttings.

Stately old-growth ponderosa pines once ruled the lower southern flanks of Mount Adams. They were found in open, grassy meadows because of frequent, low-intensity wildfires. The biggest "yellow-bellies" were in the age range of three hundred to five hundred years old. The original pine forest covered a relatively vast area that extended between the White Salmon and Klickitat River drainages. North of Trout Lake, Washington's largest ponderosa pine—almost seven feet thick and more than two hundred feet tall—died in 2016, likely from an infestation of western pine beetle.

As kids, Darvel and I would play among the huge trees. Back then, the big pines were selectively logged by J. Neils Lumber Company and other private firms, as well as the Washington Department of Natural Resources and the U.S. Forest Service. We remember trainloads of thick ponderosa logs heading to the Klickitat mill on a narrow-gauge railway that belonged to the J. Neils company. The tracks crossed the Mount Adams Highway about a mile north of our home in Glenwood, and log trains would pass by as we waited for the school bus. The ponderosa pine forest has changed in character and structure. Other species, such as grand fir, Douglas fir, and western larch became established, and their density has greatly increased (in terms of stems per acre). However, there are still sizeable numbers of scattered, old-growth yellow-bellies north of Trout Lake in Gifford Pinchot National Forest, and on Washington DNR land northwest of Glenwood.

In early 2018, Forest Service District Ranger Emily Platt approved the Upper White Salmon River Restoration Project, an area that covers more than seven thousand acres on the southern slopes of Mount Adams in the Pinchot. Commercial thinning and other treatments are intended to protect the remaining old-growth, and "restore and increase resilience to disturbance from fire, insects, and disease in the upper White Salmon River watershed." Only time will tell if the ambitious plan will succeed.

Chapter 13

Mount St. Helens Erupts

Going through something catastrophic shows you how short life is and how precious things are.
— William Dilley

Before 1980, Mount St. Helens was an imposing, near-perfect cone that soared a vertical mile above timberline to 9,677 feet. Darvel and I climbed it a few times during the 1970s, starting from the popular Timberline Viewpoint at 4,360 feet. The low elevation of tree line and loose pumice soils were the result of pyroclastic flows from summit dome eruptions between the mid-1600s and late 1700s. The eruptive period between 1800 and 1857 constructed the Goat Rocks dacite dome on the northern flank, well below the ice-filled summit crater.

A USGS bulletin in 1978 warned that Mount St. Helens' next eruption " . . . is likely to occur within the next hundred years, and perhaps even before the end of this century." But until the third week of March in 1980, there was no indication that the 123-year dormant period was about to end. Then, on March 27, after a week of hundreds of earthquakes under the mountain, a phreatic explosion of steam and dark ash formed a 250-foot wide crater on the summit. Fresh fissures bisected the summit plateau, and on the northern edge, fractures appeared near the False Summit. At the Glenwood School, my wife Susan and her third- and fourth-grade students clearly heard the midday explosion. I was out of reach of all news on a multi-day mountain medicine seminar in Yosemite National Park.

Through April, residents in Washington and Oregon were constantly preoccupied with the volcano's ominous activity. I imagined forests below Mount St. Helens burning from fresh lava while mudflows poured down the Toutle River. Earthquakes increased in intensity and a huge bulge expanded on the volcano's north side. Two craters enlarged to become one, and the whole area subsided as a graben. Frequent steam explosions erupted

dark ash. We devoured every new article and photo that appeared daily in the *Oregonian*. When would it blow? Would Harry Truman—the Spirit Lake resident who refused to evacuate—survive? Radio chatter was full of speculation.

I wanted to get telephotos of St. Helens from the east, but there was a deep snowpack blocking roads. In early April, Harold Cole and I skied to an overlook in Indian Heaven, about twenty miles from the mountain. We could hear muffled explosions, but low clouds obscured our view. About a week later on a clear day, our friend Bill Gillanders took us up in his small plane. We flew over Mount Margaret and Spirit Lake to within five miles of the darkened volcano. I photographed the massive bulge and ominous fractures on the north face. Before the flight I had toyed with the idea of illegally climbing Mount St. Helens from the south. Now I wanted to stay far away from this transformed and obviously dangerous volcano.

The catastrophic eruption of Mount St. Helens began finally at 8:32 A.M. on May 18, 1980. It had been a beautiful, peaceful Sunday morning when the entire north side collapsed into two enormous landslides, followed by a third minutes later. A magnitude 5.1 earthquake occurred at the same time. The sudden release of pressure on rising magma and hot fluids created immense explosions of gas and rock, heard hundreds of miles away (but not closer than about sixty miles from the volcano). The blasts transformed into *pyroclastic density flows* of 600°F gases mixed with steam, rocks, and coarse ash. Laterally directed toward the north, west, and east, the density flows were described by geologist Richard Waitt as " . . . searing surges of doom [that reached] out 10 to

In pre-eruption years, Mount St. Helens was an imposing, near-perfect cone that soared a vertical mile above timberline to 9,677 feet.

18 miles, mowing down forests, killing all in the way." The landslides resulted in the largest debris avalanche in recorded history. Almost two-thirds of a cubic mile of volcanic debris and glacier ice filled the Toutle Valley below, up to 600 feet deep.

The ground-hugging surges leveled more than 230 square miles and killed fifty-seven people, including Harry Truman in his home at the edge of Spirit Lake; most died from ash asphyxiation. No one could have imagined the holocaust. Richard Waitt's gripping book, *In the Path of Destruction*, provides remarkable insight and clarity as to what actually happened. The large book has riveting eyewitness accounts and new information, photos, and maps. After thirty-five years, I finally understand the awesome hydrogen-bomb-like photograph by Marshall Hunting, taken in the Cowlitz Valley around eight-fifty that morning.

About ten minutes after the initial explosions, density surges slowed, having destroyed an area ten times the size of Manhattan Island. The immense blanket of hot gasses and less dense material—ash, sand, silt, and forest litter—then shot *straight upward* from the devastated landscape at a rate of about a thousand feet per minute. Day turned to night. Ash and debris pelted the ground, and lightning went berserk. The roiling twenty-mile-wide column broadened into a mushroom forty-five miles wide, topping out at 80,000 feet. It was centered well north and west of the volcano's crater. Only a weak plume drifted above Mount St. Helens' crater at the time. But the small plume soon grew into a dark, vertical eruption column. By 9:25 A.M., the classic cauliflower column over the volcano's crater reached six miles high and joined the easterly drift of the much higher plume that preceded it. Wood debris and dark ash fell on Mount Adams and Mount Rainier. Carried east–northeast by strong upper level winds, the center of the eruption plume passed directly over the Goat Rocks Wilderness and Yakima. In eastern Washington the deepest ash—nearly three inches—fell near Ritzville.

Pyroclastic flows up to 1,500°F swept down all sides of the volcano, but they were most concentrated on the breached north side. On the upper Toutle plain, water and glacial ice trapped under hot flow deposits flashed into steam and exploded into miniature eruptions and craters. Massive mudflows (or lahars) down the lower Toutle River valley destroyed dozens of homes and blocked the Columbia River to shipping. Destructive lahars also descended river drainages east, south, and west of the volcano.

The eruption grew to its greatest intensity in late afternoon. The ash column over the crater widened and became more turbulent. By five that afternoon, the roiling column reached 63,000 feet. Finally during the evening, the great eruption of May 18, 1980, slackened off.

On that fateful Sunday morning, Susan and I had slept in. We were at home next to the Flying L Ranch. Blue skies overhead and bright sunshine flooded our front meadow, promising a lovely, warm day. At around nine o'clock, I noticed that the sky toward the northwest was filled with an ominous, inky darkness. Seeing lightning and hearing a steady rumbling of thunder, I thought it was odd that a thunderstorm was approaching from that direction. Moments later, a climber friend and neighbor, Greg Page, called and told us that Mount St. Helens had erupted. "It's the big one!" Greg said in a rush. I grabbed my camera (never without film) and took a few quick shots of Mount Adams disappearing in the huge, black ash cloud. I called my mother at the Flying L and relayed the momentous news. I said we would pick her up in ten minutes to view the eruption from a high point at the edge of the Glenwood Valley. Into the car we threw in some food and water, including towels to breathe through in case we were caught in ash fall.

The once-blue skies overhead turned into a thick overcast of cirrostratus clouds in a matter of minutes, apparently because of the sudden increase in air temperature and pressure at higher altitudes.

With others from Glenwood, we watched the eruption until early evening from the Diamond Gap lookout site, a 3,000-foot knoll about forty miles southeast of St. Helens. Mount Adams was barely visible in the dark gloom, and lightning flashes were frequent in that direction. The mountain had been enveloped in ash for only

From a small plane in March 1980, Mount Margaret Backcountry and Spirit Lake provides foreground for the ominous-appearing volcano, which awakened from dormancy after 123 years.

Around nine o'clock on the morning of Sunday, May 18, 1980, Mount Adams disappears in the forty-mile-wide ash cloud—generated by massive density currents that rose above the devastated landscape north of St. Helens.

Later in the day, we watch the cataclysmic eruption from the top of Diamond Gap, a high point above Camas Prairie. A strange sulfurous fog begins to fill the valleys.

Chris Krueger views it through his telescope. During the foreboding day, a large group of Glenwood Valley folks gather on the knoll.

Cloudy and wet weather follows, and a few days later, an ash-covered Mount Adams emerges. The photo is from the deck of my home.

about a half-hour earlier in the day. We had a great view of the dark plume spreading endlessly across the eastern horizon of central Washington. There was no ash fallout in Glenwood on May 18, but Darvel's car and front porch in the Colorado Rockies received a good dusting.

By midday more people arrived at the hilltop to watch the show—a once-in-a-lifetime event if ever there was one. It was almost like a party, because we had as yet heard no news of fatalities or devastation on a portable radio that someone shared. Several people brought telescopes, and we took turns watching the roiling ash rise out of Mount St. Helens' new crater.

In the afternoon, a strange, sulfurous fog moved in from the north and filled both Trout Lake and Glenwood valleys. The sulfur smell was strong on the valley floor as we drove home late in the day. I knew that volcanic eruptions produce sulfur dioxide and other sulfur compounds, and that the fog (or *vog*) could be a toxic mix of minute water droplets and sulfuric acid. I remember saying that it was best for all of us to stay inside our homes until the air cleared. Some Glenwood people were playing baseball as we passed through town. I would have warned them, but I wasn't sure if the air was toxic enough to be of concern. In any case, no locals seemed to be affected, and by the next morning the volcanic smog was gone.

Several days of cloudy and wet weather passed before we saw Mount Adams again. When it finally came out, the mountain looked like it had been spray-painted a uniformly gray color. A recent ice avalanche left a white streak down the middle part of Klickitat Glacier. About the same time, President Jimmy Carter toured the upper Toutle landscape near Mount St. Helens and said it made the moon look like a golf course. Earlier he had declared the State of Washington a major disaster area. The same day that the president arrived in Portland, I was detouring around the traffic jams to pick up a carload of food for our summer season of the Mount Adams Wilderness Institute.

Susan and I, along with four close friends in the valley, were anxious to backpack high on Mount Adams to get views of the mind-blowing changes around Mount St. Helens. On Saturday, May 24, we drove as high as we could on the Bird Creek Road (about the 4,000-foot level) and headed up the long south slope of Adams on

From our camp at 7,800 feet on South Butte, we observe the first rays of the morning sun illuminating the plume of the May 25 St. Helens eruption.

ash-covered snow. The gritty ash gave us good traction on the deep snowpack. We reached the top of South Butte cinder cone, at about 7,800 feet, in thick fog, and set up camp on the western edge of the small crater. I used a compass to position our tent opening toward due west where I knew there was a good view of St. Helens in clear weather.

Around 3:00 A.M. on Sunday, May 25, I looked out of our tent and saw a lot of lightning in the dark sky to the west. "Hey, it's erupting again!" I yelled, waking up our friends in the two other tents. We slumbered until it was light enough to see a thick column of ash rising above a solid layer of low clouds that obscured the actual volcano. Relieved that ash wasn't heading in our direction, I got up and started taking photos. Soon the rising sun illuminated the upper part of the cauliflower-shaped eruption plume, which rose as high as 25,000 feet. Later, lenticular cap clouds formed over the dense plume. Upper-level winds carried most of the ash northwest over the Centralia–Chahalis area and Olympic Peninsula. Lower-level winds spread minor amounts of ash southward toward Vancouver and Portland. Dense fog filled all of western Washington and into Oregon, grounding all aircraft on the west side of the Cascades.

With the May 25 eruption continuing through mid-morning, we explored the higher slopes of Mount Adams' southern flank. We came across tracks of frightened climbers, who had rushed down the mountain a week earlier on May 18. By all accounts, no climbers were injured, but they were obviously unnerved by the immensity of the event: darkness, gritty ash pelting them, frequent lightning, the abrupt thirty-plus-degree rise in air temperature, and pieces of charred wood falling from the sky. We found many wood chunks and Douglas fir branches up to three feet long on the broad snowfields above nine thousand feet. Smelling of charred wood, the debris was buoyed by hot gasses and ash that rose from the huge surge-blasted area, carrying it about forty miles in the upper atmosphere to land on the slopes of Adams.

Months later, I learned that because of the dense fog and grounded aircraft, very few other people, if any, witnessed and photographed the May 25, 1980, eruption. The USGS apparently had no photos of it. So I made duplicate slides of the entire sequence and sent them to the Denver office. In return I was given the 844-page, eight-pound USGS Professional Paper 1250, published in late 1981. It's a fascinating compilation of research papers in book form titled, *The 1980 Eruptions of Mount St. Helens, Washington*.

A lenticular cap cloud forms over the dense ash plume of the May 25 eruption, while fog fills the low country. Upper-level winds carry the ash in a northwesterly direction.

Mountain goat tracks in the pumice are the only sign of animal life on the north side of Adams in August 1980.

National Geographic purchased a photo that I took with our tent in the foreground. The image was scheduled for a page-and-a-half in size, but John Christiansen's amazing sequential photos taken from Pikers Peak on Mount Adams usurped mine. Still, I was paid six hundred dollars—way more than enough to buy a new Nikon 35mm camera.

Following the May 25 eruption, the Forest Service and Yakama Tribe closed the Mount Adams area to all use until further notice. The closures, as well as the uncertainty of continued eruptions, forced me to cancel all Mount Adams Wilderness Institute sessions scheduled for the coming summer. We had been completely booked up with full payments received, and I had purchased all of the non-perishable food needed for the season. It was a financial blow, but I was still optimistic that the Institute would survive. It would have been our eleventh year in operation.

An aerial photo in August 1980 captures the transformed landscape north of Mount St. Helens, with the west face of Mount Adams in the background.

In August 1980, I received permission from the Forest Service to drive around to the north side of Mount Adams. Deposits of tephra (explosively ejected fragments) were much thicker on the north side of mountain. I photographed mountain goat tracks in the fresh pumice near Potato Hill. Swollen glacier streams were a dark chocolate color like I'd never seen before. The thin layer of ash darkened glacier surfaces and permanent snowfields, absorbing solar radiation much more rapidly than normal. Avalanche Glacier, in particular, was never the same after the melt season of 1980.

Continued eruptions throughout that fall led to administrative closures of the Mount Adams area within the Gifford Pinchot National Forest and Yakama Indian Reservation through 1981. Despite my spirited protests both verbally and in numerous letters, both the Forest Service and Yakama Nation maintained their indefinite closures of the mountain. I felt that many risks and dangers existed in wilderness areas, and that the risk of ash fallout would just be one of them. It would have been inconvenient and unpleasant, but not life-threatening. My arguments, however, fell on deaf ears. With indefinite closures, we couldn't plan ahead and had no choice but to end the Mount Adams Wilderness Institute.

It also changed the direction of my life. I returned to seafaring, and soon afterward obtained my unlimited master mariner's license. By the end of the 1980s, I sailed as master on seven ships of various types and sizes. I piloted ships mostly between Seattle and the Alaska Peninsula, Aleutian Islands, and Bering Sea—and as far south as the Galapagos Islands on the oceanographic research vessel *Thomas G. Thompson*. In Alaskan waters I would frequently pass by active volcanoes. I was delighted when spells of clear weather would reveal the smoking cones of heavily glaciated volcanoes, like splendid Mount Shishaldin on Unimak Island. My camera was always handy. Besides their sheer beauty, the volatility of volcanoes had become another thread in the weave of my life.

Steam rises out of St. Helens' crater during a flight around the volcano in December 1980.

PART THREE

EVER WILD

Chapter 14

Climbing Ice

Security is when everything is settled, when nothing can happen to you. Security is the denial of life.
— Germaine Greer

Darvel and I accomplished our most challenging snow and ice climbs in the Cascades during the 1970s. It was a golden age of mountaineering for us, and perfect timing for our Mount Adams Wilderness Institute summer programs. Not only were glaciers bigger back then, but they appeared more beautiful and were far safer to climb. During spring months, we usually pulled off as much technical snow and ice climbing as we could squeeze in on Adams, Hood, and other Cascade peaks. Darvel had to cut back as my climbing partner in the late 1970s because of a job he landed in Colorado. But by the decade's end, I had ascended nine different routes on Mount Adams; not always to the summit, because the goal was to do the most difficult parts.

During the 1970s and into the '80s, I was a member of the Alpinees mountain rescue group in Hood River, and I took part in some dramatic winter rescues, especially on Mount Hood. One particular rescue attempt on Mount Adams will be forever etched in my memory.

Keith Edwards was an incredibly strong climber, a brilliant pre-med student in Portland and a good friend. In February 1973, he and his climbing partner, Duane Hess, were killed while descending Lyman Glacier on the northeast face of Mount Adams. I was the last person to see them alive. They had stopped at our house en route to the east side, so I knew their plans were to ski to Avalanche Valley, make camp, and then do an east-face route, possibly Victory Ridge. They had never been on that side of the mountain, so I gave them detailed instructions on the best route to their objective.

Keith left a borrowed CB base radio and said that he would try to make contact each evening at seven. I listened and never heard a word from him. But knowing that CB radios were only good for line-of-sight communication, I wasn't overly concerned. Avalanche Valley and much of the east face were hidden from Glenwood by Battlement and Victory ridges.

When Duane's family in Portland reported the two climbers overdue, I joined a large search-and-rescue effort that was organized and based at the Flying L Ranch. Glenwood snowmobilers were very helpful in following the climbers' ski tracks to their unoccupied tent in Avalanche Valley. A military helicopter transported mountain rescue teams to the shoulder of Goat Butte on the east side of Adams. We made our base camp in deep snow on flat ground, sheltered by whitebark pines. For several days we searched a wide area on the east and northeast sides of Mount Adams with no success. The weather was very cold, but otherwise favorable. Eventually, their tracks were found leading up the Wilson Glacier headwall, indicating that Keith and Duane had made a first ascent of the route in perfect snow and cold-temperature conditions.

A day later, Duane's body was found on the south icefall of Lyman Glacier, hidden from our view by a rock buttress between the glaciers. He was attached to a climbing rope, which led to my conclusion that, while cramponing down the Lyman icefall, one climber fell and dragged the other down the steep ice slope. Later, searchers found Keith's body next to a house-size, brecciated boulder in Devils Garden. One leg was crudely splinted with his ice axe, indicating that he had made an incredibly brave struggle to reach that spot. Devils Garden is an area of alpine tundra, well above the tree line. Keith had

In September 1976, I lead three clients on a climb of the Adams Glacier icefall. Mount St. Helens is in the background.

Left: In the spring of 1976, Darvel climbs quickly below an ice pinnacle that we called "The Big Serac," on the north Klickitat icefall. *Right:* Once above the serac, Darvel moves more slowly and carefully up the steeper sections of the icefall.

apparently died of hypothermia, complicated by injuries. The radio was found with him, so he might have tried to call me from that spot. I had heard nothing when I listened to the loaned base radio that night.

A week or so later I met with Keith's parents. One of the hardest things I've ever had to do in my life was to explain to them what I thought had happened, in as much detail as possible. I felt that their son could not have lasted the night because of the bitterly cold weather and his lack of shelter or bivouac gear. Regarding the radio, I said that Keith couldn't possibly reach me from that side of the mountain. The climbers were completely unfamiliar with the descent route, and were roped when they fell. However, they had not placed a solid anchor to stop a fall, and were not prepared for an emergency in midwinter on such a remote and rugged part of Mount Adams.

In 1976 and 1977, Darvel and I climbed both north and south Klickitat icefalls on cold spring mornings. Both would be three-day efforts because of the long ski trips to the base. I had studied the two routes with binoculars from my home in Glenwood. Before our 1976 south icefall climb, binoculars weren't needed to spot a gigantic vertical ice pinnacle, which we called The Big Serac. Standing in the middle of our route, it was about one hundred fifty feet tall and had formed a few weeks earlier. The pinnacle cast an ominous shadow on the glacier. We wondered if climbing beneath it was worth the risk, then quickly decided, "Damned right!"

The morning of the climb dawned cold and clear from Sunrise Camp, a windswept saddle at eighty-three hundred feet between Klickitat and Mazama glaciers. We cramponed up the hard ice quickly—as fast as we had ever climbed in our lives—foregoing ice-screw anchors or belays to save time. It was a race against the morning sun. Sunshine bathed The Big Serac. We knew that rising temperatures would eventually cause rocks to fall, and seracs, including the big one, to fracture without warning. When that happens, the icefall would become a deadly bowling alley with no conceivable way to escape.

Darvel reaches the crest of Adams upon our completion of the first direct ascent of the summit headwall.

Fortunately, we encountered no falling debris on that climb, nor was there rockfall on our beautiful ascent of the south Klickitat icefall the following year. About a week after our north icefall ascent, The Big Serac toppled over and avalanched down the glacier. I gulped when I saw the result from my living room window in Glenwood. But I knew that because of freezing temperatures, we had timed our climb just fine. The serac was historic in size. I've never seen another ice pinnacle like it in the Cascades.

Adams Glacier is the largest, longest, and most beautiful of the mountain's glaciers. It captures much of the summit icecap and gradually flows northwesterly across buried craters and active fumaroles. Where it spills over the steep northwest face, the glacier transforms into a spectacular 2,800-foot icefall of a jumble of crevasses and seracs. Because of its relatively rapid movement of up to several feet per day, the Adams icefall can change significantly from year to year, and from early summer to late fall.

In September of 1976, I led three clients on a climb of the Adams Glacier icefall. It was frozen hard and was typically broken up for that time of year. Ice screws were needed for protection on most of the climb. A huge crevasse blocked our route at about the 11,000-foot level, but I eventually found a way to ease myself down to a platform and scale the opposite wall. The difficult technical climbing consumed too much time, and we turned back short of the summit. While on our descent of the North Cleaver, my clients suffered extreme fatigue. It was well into the night when I finally got the three men back to their campsite in Glacier Basin. Their wives had built a campfire as a beacon, and it proved helpful for the poor guys stumbling in on their last legs.

In the meantime, I had a job commitment to join a ship in Tacoma as chief mate by eight the very next morning. In the middle of the night, I literally ran the last four miles down through the forest to my car. Then I drove, way too fast, back to Glenwood, which was on the opposite side of the mountain. With no time to even

Left: Adams Glacier icefall spills 2,800 feet down the northwest face. An arrow shows where I photographed the big crevasse that's pictured at right.

take a shower, I packed for the delivery job to Alaska and somehow made the four-hour drive to Tacoma, arriving at my ship—the 340-foot MV *Royal Venture*—shortly after sunrise with barely an hour to spare. But our departure on the voyage was postponed, fortunately for me, until the following day. After being up for sixty hours (except for a couple of hours of dozing at camp the first night) and utterly exhausted, I finally got some real sleep.

During the 1970s, the deepest crevasses on Adams Glacier were on the relatively flat area below the icefall at about 8,800 feet. They were perfect for crevasse rescue practice for our Mount Adams Wilderness Institute groups. One time I rappelled down to the bottom of an 80-foot crevasse. It was midday, and the sun's rays happened to reach the floor at the same time that I took a few photos. I remember marveling at the dense walls of

greenish blue ice. Except for my breathing and the dripping of melt water, there were no other sounds. Using old-fashioned prusik (friction) slings, I climbed back up the anchored rope and squirmed over the crevasse lip to my waiting group.

Always with belays, our participants learned several techniques of getting someone out of both hidden and open crevasses. During crevasse-rescue practice, each person would play the role of a fallen climber hanging on a rope with prusik slings handy. (Mechanical ascenders now do the job far more efficiently.) On Rusk Glacier, our clients were taught climbing techniques on what we considered safe seracs, located on a stable icefall on the south side of the glacier. It was well clear of the rockfall zone below The Castle or Roosevelt Cliff.

In August 2014, I intently studied Mount Adams' east face with binoculars from Avalanche Valley, and was

Top left: Rappelling down to the bottom of a deep crevasse, the only sounds were my breathing and the drips of meltwater.

Above: One of my clients, a big-animal veterinarian from Idaho, took this shot of me attempting to find a route around a huge crevasse. We eventually had to scale the opposite wall. (Darryl Lloyd Collection)

Left: Just as the midday sun hit the bottom, I looked up toward the lip of the crevasse, about eighty feet or more above me.

In the spring of 1977, Darvel and I climbed the south Klickitat icefall. When he took this photo I was sucking an icicle for hydration. The climb got "interesting" at this point.

After our south icefall climb, we returned to Sunrise Camp. In our absence, a snowmobiler had left tracks within a few feet of our tent.

Below: Darvel ponders a vertical pitch on the south Klickitat icefall in 1977.

alarmed by how thin Rusk Glacier had become. A vast island of exposed bedrock was splitting the glacier in half. Another patch of bedrock appeared below the diminished icefall that we had practiced on.

The prime climbing conditions that we had on Northwest glaciers during the 1970s have been absent for decades. Climate change has made steep snow and ice climbing a hundred times more dangerous. Icefalls, headwalls, and glaciers have much greater rockfall now. Most of the seracs are gone, and the small ones that remain can collapse at any time during summer months. Snow bridges are untrustworthy, even at night. The large, deep crevasses at 8,800 feet on Adams Glacier may have shrunk to half their original depths. Falling rocks in that area might now make it unsafe for a group focused on crevasse rescue.

I've heard that obstacles in your life are your journey. But risks that were acceptable during the 1970s simply would not be taken today, even if I happened to be fifty years younger and had the same vigor and passions. Nonetheless, the yesteryears of the '70s were a remarkable part of my life's journey on Mount Adams.

Chapter 15

The Great East Side

The super-feature of Mount Adams, the thing that makes it truly great and places it in the front rank of the grand mountains on earth, is the incomparable eastern side.

— C. E. Rusk

C. E. Rusk gave it the name "Great East Side" back in 1919. There was a mystique about the name when Darvel and I were growing up in Glenwood. We heard stories of Avalanche Valley from our Flying L Ranch foreman Ed Jones, who had packed people into the area by horseback decades earlier. Occasionally we would get glimpses of the broad east face when our parents drove us across the Yakama Reservation in our 1951 Chrysler. The reservation was open to the public at the time (but closed soon after), and we would take the dirt road across the forested eastern flanks of the mountain between Glenwood and Potato Hill. During our pre-teen years, we hiked to the top of Little Mount Adams and got a better sense of the rugged corner of the east face. But most of our knowledge of this grand and hidden side of Mount Adams came from our parents' copy of Rusk's *Tales of a Western Mountaineer.* Avalanche Valley was an alluring place, and no one would take us there.

At the edge of the Great East Side facing Glenwood, Mazama Glacier was very accessible from Bird Creek Meadows. We began climbing this moderate glacier route when we were upper classmen in high school. Our favorite part of the ascent was cramponing up the hard ice of Early Morning Ridge. In the golden light of the rising sun, we loved to look northward across the precipices and icefalls of the Klickitat headwall. After reaching the summit, we always walked over to the eastern rim and gazed down upon the icecap and The Castle. Far below—framing a drop of almost 6,000 vertical feet—was the small green vale of Avalanche Valley. It was a favorite base camp of Rusk for his many explorations of the east face. We knew

that after high-school graduation, we would realize our dream to reach Avalanche Valley.

So in 1961, at eighteen years of age, we made our first backpacking traverse into the heart of the east side—at the time, all within Mount Adams Wild Area of Gifford Pinchot National Forest. Planning a four-day trip, we had basic climbing gear, but inadequate backpacks and only a tarp for shelter. We chose the high route over Klickitat Glacier from Bird Creek Meadows. Even though the terrain was rough and unfamiliar, the route was fairly straightforward across the glacier. We had no problems picking our way around Battlement Ridge and across the broad basin below Rusk Glacier. I'll always remember entering Avalanche Valley for the first time and plopping down in the warm grass to simply marvel at the majestic east face. We identified the features that C. E. Rusk named four decades earlier, and tracked Rusk's first ascent route. That trip marked the beginning of fifty-five years of exploration and reverence for the Great East Side of Mount Adams.

Avalanche Valley is a flowered meadow occupying a 6,600-foot bench at the western base of Goat Butte. It's an oasis in the midst of harshness. On this dry side of the mountain, sagebrush thrives on slopes next to the valley. The fragile meadow offers fabulous views of the east face. I loved to relax in the shade of whispering whitebark pines and listen to the rushing stream, which begins from springs at the head of the valley. The last time I was there, in August 2014, I heard a few whistles of a hoary marmot and the "eep" of an American pika on the talus slope nearby. But in recent decades and due to climate

The sprawling east face of Mount Adams is best revealed from an airplane, or alternatively from the top of Goat Butte. Bisecting the face, at center, is Battlement Ridge.

change, populations of both mammals have fallen in sub-alpine areas of the Cascades.

About half of the old-growth whitebark pines on the east side have died from the blister-rust fungus. Most of the remaining old whitebarks were killed in the Cougar Creek Fire of 2015. The reduction of whitebark pine nuts has significantly decreased the food supply of Clark's nut-cracker birds and golden-mantled ground squirrels. What a great loss to this fragile ecosystem.

A couple of bitterly cold ponds in Avalanche Valley provide nice reflections of the mountain for photography, especially at sunrise when the mountain is bathed in red light and the shadow of Goat Butte covers the valley. At the top of 7,484-foot Goat Butte are fragments of an old fire lookout that was built in 1931 and purposely destroyed with dynamite in 1965 by the Yakama Tribe. Otherwise there is no evidence of human activity in this grand scene. It is truly the kingdom of mountain goats, whose population has greatly increased over the past decade or so. In August 2014, a friend and I counted nearly one hundred mountain goats in two groups near the valley.

The sprawling east face is a sight to behold from the top of Goat Butte. Mount Adams dominates one hundred eighty degrees of the western sky from Ridge of Wonders to the south, all the way across to the North Cleaver and Red Butte. The super feature of the east face is a spectacular 1.5-mile-wide, 3,500-foot-high rampart of rock and ice. Here are the headwalls of Klickitat, Rusk, and Wilson glaciers, and some of the wildest precipices and ice cliffs in the Cascades. It's also the home to thundering avalanches. The 200-foot-thick summit icecap is draped like a glistening crown over the entire wall. It overhangs Roosevelt Cliff in places—ominously. Sooner or later great chunks of it break off. Roosevelt Cliff is near vertical with as much as 1,500 feet of relief. Ice avalanches can occur day or night in all seasons; and the deep sounds of pounding and rumbling often shatter the stillness of Avalanche Valley. Pulverized ice and rock debris make dark plumes and streaks on the glaciers below.

Crags on the massive wall are colored in hues of red, yellow, black, and gray—caused by oxidation when andesite lava flows erupted from the summit twenty thousand to thirty thousand years ago. The heart of the mountain is laid bare. In a satellite view looking straight down, Mount Adams has the strange appearance of a once-conical volcano whacked in half by a giant axe in a north-south

During on our east-side traverse in late July 2007, Darvel begins to cross the 7,800-foot flat on Klickitat Glacier. Ever-increasing rubble is exposed by midsummer and makes the trek much more difficult.

Dead whitebark pines cover the south side of Goat Butte by 2011. Most of them later burned in the Cougar Creek Fire of 2015.

direction. Over the millennia, the originally moderately angled slopes have been removed by steep glaciers, landslides, and rapid erosion.

During our climbs to high points on Rusk and Wilson glaciers, Darvel and I always kept a safe distance from Roosevelt Cliff. It seemed frightfully steep and dangerous because of avalanches and rockfall. The first ascent of Roosevelt Cliff took place in July 1963 by legendary climber Fred Becky (who lived to age ninety-four) and his companion, Don Gordon. Becky later wrote that after crossing a bergschrund at the head of Wilson Glacier, they made a two-hour traverse of the ice face with "many stones falling." They entered a prominent ice couloir on the final cliff, where progress became very slow as they cut steps, front-pointed, and belayed from lateral ledges of rock. The crux of the climb came next. Becky wrote in *Challenge of the North Cascades* (1969):

> Late in the afternoon we reached a strange safety, climbing right up under hanging icicles of the final ice cliff. Staying behind the icicle curtain much of the time, protected by ice and rock pitons and some natural hummocks, we now cut steps leftward for three leads. At last we chopped across a section of blue ice where we could look directly down rotten exposed cliffs, to the Rusk Glacier. An easy 200-foot ice slope tapered toward the true summit.

The jagged spine of Battlement Ridge is the most rugged and prominent high ridge on Mount Adams. Splitting the east face, it rises steeply between Klickitat and Rusk glaciers. The ridge begins at around 7,000 feet and ends at the top of The Castle at 11,450 feet, an imposing, 1,200-foot high promontory that looms over the east face. Gendarmes (rock pinnacles) along the narrow Battlement Ridge add to the challenge for climbers. Some pinnacles were created by the great Klickitat rock avalanche of 1997, when a 1,500-foot high, five-million-cubic-yard slab of hydrothermally altered rock broke off and thundered three miles down the valley. It left a fresh, multicolored scar on the south-facing side of the ridge between 9,700 and 11,200 feet. Andesite lava here is part of Mount Adams' central core. It became rotten during thousands of years of exposure to sulfur-bearing gases, hot water, and steam. Wise climbers stay clear.

On the southern end of the wall are the north and south icefalls of Klickitat Glacier, separated by the eastern precipices and also known as the Klickitat headwall. The Klickitat Glacier amphitheater is one of the largest glacier cirques in the Cascade Range, ranking behind the Carbon Glacier cirque on Mount Rainier.

Probably no other glacier in the Cascades can surpass the Klickitat in rockfall. By the end of the summer season,

A pond in Avalanche Valley reflects the morning sun on the east face in 2007. Rusk Glacier lies at center, The Spearhead at left, and reddish Victory Ridge at right.

the glacier surface becomes an awful mess of rock and debris. Big Muddy Creek drains the glacier—the largest and muddiest stream on Mount Adams. The canyon of the Big Muddy is the mountain's deepest, and very few people ever see it by foot.

At a modest 8,300 feet, The Spearhead is a 1,000-foot high, yellowish-brown pinnacle on a northern spur of Battlement Ridge. It is brecciated dacite lava, a remnant of the half-million-year-old Hellroaring Volcano, which also outcrops higher on the south side of Battlement Ridge. On my many traverses of the east side during the 1970s, I thought the pinnacle looked like a projectile point or a spearhead when viewed from Avalanche Valley. I went through the official steps with the U.S. Board of Geographic Names to establish its present name of The Spearhead. Long ago a Boy Scout Troop from Yakima intended to name the pinnacle "Battlement Peak," but like many informal names, it faded along with scout memories.

On a geologic timescale, the erosional process from ice and gravity has been exceedingly rapid. Layers of andesite lava are rubbly and brecciated, and the uppermost headwalls are hydrothermally altered. Nothing is very solid on the Great East Side. Early writers were fooled into thinking that Mount Adams was an extinct volcano of old and scarred basalt, long past its slumbering stage. Little did they know of the reddish vent on Battlement Ridge that erupted andesite lava and cinders perhaps as recently as a few hundred years ago.

Very few hikers get close to this part of the mountain's east side; and only one trail, the Highline Trail, leads into the area from the north. The off-trail traverse from Bird Creek Meadows to the valley is a major undertaking. Completely within the Yakama Reservation since 1972, it is known by some as "The Gap," but the name seems pedestrian and I don't use it. Only strong, experienced off-trail backpackers and speed hikers should consider the crossing. Over the decades, Darvel and I have made some *seventy* backpacking traverses by the high route. Many were during the ten-year period during the 1970s, when we led our Mount Adams Wilderness Institute groups. My last traverse was in 2014.

Springs gush forth at the head of the valley. *Below:* The species "mountain big sagebrush" is found as high as 7,200 feet on the east side of Adams.

I wouldn't recommend attempting the high route beyond late July in normal snowpack years because climate warming has made it far more difficult and demanding. There has been a loss of fifty feet or more of once permanent snow and ice thickness along the route. Formerly dependable snowfields on the slog to Sunrise saddle have melted, exposing tricky boulder fields. The loss of ice on the lower Klickitat Glacier exposed a long stretch of unstable rubble, and two trekking poles are

a must. An ice axe isn't necessary, but crampons might be. Most of the lower glacier is now stagnant ice and the small remnant crevasses are obvious. The high route can be done in a day; however, crossing Rusk Creek in the afternoon on warm days might be a problem.

Traversing the east side by the low route over the Ridge of Wonders is more direct and the cumulative elevation gain is less. But the terrain is steeper and rougher, and crossing the Big Muddy can be dangerous in warm weather.

A raven could fly from The Spearhead due south across the Klickitat Glacier basin and land on the crest of Ridge of Wonders, also at 8,300 feet. Here is the best place for a human to view Klickitat Glacier. From this seldom-visited viewpoint, the entire 4,000-foot headwall is exposed in all of its grandeur. Awed by the view in the late 1890s, C. E. Rusk named Ridge of Wonders.

This great ridge is about all that remains of the earliest lava flows on Mount Adams, over a half-million years ago. About sixty thousand years ago, Little Mount Adams erupted andesite lava, scoria, and agglutinate on the south side of Ridge of Wonders. From the reddish cinder-spatter cone, the ridge sweeps grandly upward. It narrows, becomes jagged and curves to the right around a steep cirque. Capping the yellowish-brown ridge, where Rusk contemplated the view, is an "unconformity" of much younger andesite lava, roughly thirty thousand years in age and distinctively gray in color.

Over the years, we've led many hiking groups up Little Mount Adams and beyond to a spectacular 6,840-foot ledge on the northern edge of Ridge of Wonders. It's a superb place to contemplate Klickitat Glacier and Big Muddy canyon. From a trailhead at Bench Lake, the historic Island Spring Trail passes through a forest heavily burned in 2015. The Island, named by sheepherders, is the broad flank bounded by Hellroaring and Big Muddy creeks. Insects and pathogens have killed off significant numbers of old-growth whitebark pine as well as lodgepole pine on The Island's upper reaches. I hope that someday the Island Spring Trail can be restored from fire damage and extended to the top of Little Mount Adams. A route up the cone had been flagged more than a decade ago, but by 2015 was nearly obliterated.

During Rusk's time, the highest road on Mount Adams east side ended at Soda Ford on the Klickitat River. This

Darvel, left, and I celebrate our return to Avalanche Valley in 2007.

was many years before the forested part of the Yakama Reservation was closed to non-tribal members. Reaching Avalanche Valley required a two-day horseback ride by way of Mount Adams Lake, the largest lake on the mountain. Sheep grazing was the main use of the high country by non-Indians, and Mount Adams had no protection from overgrazing. Dismayed by the degradation, Rusk joined a Yakima Commercial Club campaign in 1919 to promote a national park for a large part of the mountain—all within Yakima County. Grazing would be disallowed. The proposed park headquarters, including a hotel, would be located in Avalanche Valley and accessed by a new branch road off the "Mount Adams Highway."

Passing through Glenwood and the heart of the Yakama Reservation, the planned Mount Adams Highway was touted as the fastest route between Portland and Yakima. The national park proposal failed in Congress during the following year. Nevertheless, in 1922, the Mount Adams Highway—actually a dirt road—was

completed. It passed by Signal Peak, well to the east of Mount Adams, but it failed as a major route. Only a year later, Portland and Yakima were linked by a new longer but faster highway over Satus Pass. Around the early 1950s, the Yakama Nation closed most of the reservation to non-tribal members, and fortunately for the greater conservation of the area, the road to Avalanche Valley was never built. A now-abandoned jeep road provided access to the tribal lookout on top of Goat Butte between 1931 and 1965.

As to the expansion of the Yakama Reservation in 1972 to include the eastern side of Mount Adams: In the 1930s, a misplaced sketch map—called the Treaty Map and signed by Washington Territorial Governor Isaac Stevens in 1855—was found in U.S. Interior Department files and documented as authentic. The reservation boundary on the sketch map was represented by a dotted line, which appeared to loop around the upper slopes of Mount Adams. Previous official maps of the reservation had

A telephoto lens zooms in The Castle, at left, and Roosevelt Cliff, center and right. The summit icecap spectacularly overhangs the cliffs.

excluded the mountain. The Treaty's wording had been vague and contained impossible statements on geography. The recovered Treaty Map, however, gave credence to a Yakama Nation claim to 121,466 acres (the original "Tract D") on the southern and eastern slopes of Mount Adams. In 1966, the Indian Claims Commission ruled that the Treaty of 1855 had intended for the tract's inclusion the Yakama Reservation. A 1971 Yakama Tribal Resolution pledged to " . . . maintain existing recreation facilities for public use and to recognize the dedication of that portion included in the wilderness use."

After an intense public relations and legal campaign, President Richard M. Nixon in 1972 administratively transferred twenty-one thousand acres of Gifford Pinchot National Forest land on the south and east slopes of Mount Adams to the Yakama Nation. The parcel included about ten thousand acres that had been a national forest wilderness area under the 1964 Act of Congress. The new reservation boundary bisected the summit cone and took in the most rugged part of the east side. I was hired as "mountain consultant" in the summer of 1972 by the BLM Cadastral Survey, and flew to the summit by helicopter to make sure the boundary crew correctly followed the calls of the 1855 Treaty. I had my Kelty pack loaded with extra gear for survival, and I recall loaning extra clothes to the poorly equipped survey crew to keep them from freezing in the biting cold wind.

In the past decade, sixteen thousand acres of the twenty-one-thousand-acre area (named Tract D) was designated as Yakama Nation Mount Adams Recreation Area. Before the 2015 fire, it had been open to the public during the summer seasons only, normally from July 1 through September. The Recreation Area includes the Great East Side as well as the Bird Creek Meadows area and Hellroaring Valley. Much of the forested area burned in 2015.

When viewed from hills above the Yakima Valley, the broad eastern face doesn't have the shape of a typical volcano. Extending from Suksdorf Ridge to the North Cleaver, it looks more like a giant inverted soup bowl. Both south and north ridges rise gradually to a glistening, rounded summit dome, topped by a tilted cone. The hazy east face appears as a convoluted array of glaciers between dark ridges and cliffs. The impressions of steepness and grandeur are lost to the long-distance observer, but a horse-shaped formation is recognized by many Yakima Valley people. May the mystique of The Great East Side live on.

Chris Kruger of Glenwood brings along his llamas on a half-circuit of Adams in 1990. In Avalanche Valley, we celebrated the hundredth anniversary of C. E. Rusk's epic circuit along with his mother and sister.

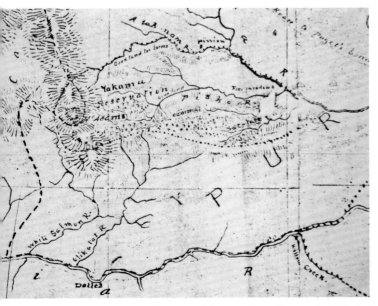

Signed by Washington's territorial Governor Isaac Stevens in 1855, the Treaty Map, shown here in a cropped reproduction, clearly indicates that the dotted line of the Yakama Reservation includes "Mt Adams." (Indian Claims Commission Archives) *Right:* Goat Butte erupted basalt about 160,000 years ago, and the permeable, stratified layers of ejecta are lightly oxidized yellowish-orange by long-ago fumaroles. C. E. Rusk would name them Castellated Cliffs.

Chapter 16

Bird Creek Meadows

Man must be able to escape civilization if he is to survive. Some of his greatest needs are for refuges and retreats where he can recapture for a day or a week the primitive conditions of life.
— William O. Douglas

Some of the happiest days of my life, beginning as a six-year-old, have been spent wandering and exploring Bird Creek Meadows on the south slope of Mount Adams. The meadows are "the brightest jewel in the wilderness tiara that encircles the mountain," said the late Keith McCoy, historian and close family friend. I concur completely. No part of the mountain is closer to my heart.

As part of the Yakama Nation Mount Adams Recreation Area, the subalpine parkland forms a triangular area between 5,700 feet and 7,150 feet, extending from the rim of Hellroaring Canyon on the east to the national forest boundary on the west. There are more than a hundred glades and meadows, and only a few are traversed by trails. The highest meadow is an exposed, boggy terrace where Mount Adams is completely hidden by a huge Mazama Glacier moraine. Fanning out below and sloping southeast are countless terraces, sandy flats, glens, hollows, and moist, flower-filled meadows. Low, rocky ridges are capped with groves of stunted whitebark pine, subalpine fir, and mountain hemlock. The dwarfed trees run parallel to the meadows and provide shelter from southwesterly winds.

A dozen or so spring-fed streams—four with names—tumble down through the meadows. The largest and my favorite is Bird Creek, which starts from multiple springs near the 7,000-foot level. The sources are not shown correctly on any map of the area, except for the 1924 USGS 30-minute quadrangle. Bird Creek bisects the meadow complex as it captures smaller streams. Crooked Creek meanders through lovely meadows and has the largest waterfalls in the area. It flows into Bird Creek west of

Bird Lake in the forested zone. Dry Creek, on the eastern edge, follows a different drainage and withers away by late summer. Near the western edge, Gotchen Creek begins as a vigorous spring about a half-mile above the Round-the-Mountain Trail. It soon splits and the larger unnamed branch flows into Bird Creek and eventually the Klickitat River. The smaller branch, keeping the Gotchen Creek name, continues south across the Yakama Reservation boundary into Gifford Pinchot National Forest. It meanders through a series of meadows—informally called Gotchen Creek Meadows since the boundary change in 1972—and ultimately flows into the White Salmon River.

One might ask why the finest floral displays on Mount Adams are found at Bird Creek Meadows. The answer is a bit involved, but first the topography. It's the result of an Ice Age piedmont glacier that, for thousands of years, spilled over and branched south from the great Hellroaring Valley glacier to scour and plane off much older dacite and andesite lava flows. Glacier scouring and polishing over the millennia made the smooth bedrock lavas impervious to water. Also, since the end of the Ice Age about 11,000 years ago, many hollows were made by *nivation*, a process of erosion beneath snow banks. Fertile soils built up in these hollows and along streams from a mix of organic material (including sheep dung) and layers of mineral-rich volcanic ash from Mount St. Helens and Mount Adams. Polished bedrock helped retain water and keep soils moist, unlike the dry porous soils and permeable lavas on other sides of the mountain. Subalpine wildflowers flourished because of constant soil moisture through dry seasons, combined with the south and southeasterly exposure to abundant

Near the beginning of Trail of the Flowers, a meadow at 6,000 feet offers a nice view of the upper Mazama and Klickitat glaciers.

sunlight. Furthermore, all of these beneficial factors likely helped the meadows recover so well (and they did) following decades of severe damage from sheep grazing.

German-born Wilhelm Suksdorf first botanized the profuse displays of wildflowers in Bird Creek Meadows in 1877. From his secluded Camas Prairie cabin, which he called *Falconthal*, Suksdorf led his packhorse along Indian trails and spent solitary weeks in the high meadows collecting plant specimens. He loved Hellroaring Valley and called it *Wodenthal* (the valley of the god). He ventured as far east on Mount Adams as the canyon of *Donnerthal* (Big Muddy Creek). Bird Creek Meadows remained unnamed until the sheepherders arrived and named the lush meadows Happy Valley.

Because of Suksdorf's quiet and gentle demeanor, area Indians befriended him. They led him on their trails, taught him their names of plants, and showed him locations of

One of the largest meadows is filled with a variety of wildflower species.

Above left: In the upper meadows toward the west, the headwaters of Bird Creek flows through a memorable display of blooms. *Left:* In a bold artistic style, pale agoseris pokes through a mat of spreading phlox. *Right:* The beautiful and interesting elephant's head thrives in moist areas of the meadows.

rare species. Suksdorf called Mount Adams "Mount Paddo" in deference to Indian usage. According to his brother Theodore, Wilhelm spent about twelve pleasurable seasons in Mount Adams' high country before the many thousands of sheep arrived with their herders. What followed, Theodore wrote, was "desolation and destruction."

Down at his cabin, Wilhelm Suksdorf catalogued more than four hundred eighty species of plants on the southeast side of Mount Adams. He visited the mountain virtually every season for fifty-five years until his death at eighty-two. He was considered one of three major pioneer botanists of the Pacific Northwest, according to his

biographer, Rhoda Love. Many plants bear the scientific name of *Suksdorfia* and *suksdorfii,* which includes at least four species in Bird Creek Meadows: showy paintbrush, buttercup, silene (campion), and bluegrass. Suksdorf Ridge, named in the mid-1950s, is the long, south shoulder (or South Spur) of Mount Adams, which extends from Pikers Peak down to South Butte.

Over the years, many other botanists have followed in Suksdorf's footsteps and made collections and lists of Mount Adams' vascular plants. In 2007, David Biek and Susan McDougall published *The Flora of Mount Adams, Washington,* which documented 830 species of woody

I call this shot "streamside flowers galore" because it's just that. The low morning sun provides perfect light.

and herbaceous plants representing eighty plant families above the 4,000-foot elevation. In an earlier booklet, McDougall wrote that the most spectacular flower show on the mountain takes place in Bird Creek Meadows.

In 2009, Paul Slichter and others with the Native Plant Society compiled a list of 162 plant species (including ten conifers) in Bird Creek Meadows alone. Slichter is a retired high-school biology teacher and has traveled widely on Mount Adams, photographing and documenting the flora. From his list, I learned that in Bird Creek Meadows there are five separate plant species within the genera paintbrush, lupine, penstemon, and sedge. There are four species in

the genera arnica, aster, buckwheat, and saxifrage. And three species exist in the genera pussytoes, monkeyflower, lousewort, and cinquefoil. That totals nearly fifty different flowering perennials in just those groups alone. Then there are all the others, which range from sharp-tooth angelica to short-fruited smelowskia.

With climate warming and decreasing snowpacks, some meadows are slowly filling in with small trees, mainly mountain hemlock and subalpine fir. This "invasion" actually began during the 1920s and 1930s, but it has been accelerating and is a phenomenon observed throughout the Cascades.

For fifty-five years, from 1877 to 1932, German-born botanist Wilhelm Suksdorf catalogued more than 480 species of plants on Mount Adams. (Wilhelm Suksdorf Papers cg315b14f89, Washington State University Libraries' MASC)

Tumbling over a ledge of 115,000-year-old dacite lava, Crooked Creek Falls is the tallest waterfall in the Bird Creek Meadows area.

Warming temperatures are also likely responsible for widespread loss of two common tree species, lodgepole pine and whitebark pine, on the south and east flanks of Mount Adams. They have been dying in Bird Creek Meadows since the early 2000s; dead snags of both species are now a common sight on tree islands in the meadows. It took about ten years for blister-rust fungus to spread from infected whitebark pines on Mount Hood to stands on Mount Adams. By 2009 on Mount Rainier, infected whitebark pines reached 78 percent. A high percentage of lodgepole pines have been killed by mountain pine beetle. Dead trees have lower moisture content than live trees, exacerbating fire; and large stands of lodgepole pine burned at high intensity in the 2015 Cougar Creek Fire, such as the area around Mirror and Bird Lakes.

When C. E. Rusk promoted national park status for Mount Adams in 1919, he was referring to Bird Creek Meadows when he wrote, "The delightful cluster of vales and meadows . . . has been appropriately called Happy Valley." Rusk added a note of sadness about the yearly destruction of the parklands by the thousands of sheep and other domestic animals that grazed to the snowline. "The witchery of the glens is helpless beneath the tread of the hoofed locusts." The Forest Service must have been influenced by Rusk's writings, because around 1919, a portion of the meadows, about 500 acres, were closed to grazing. However, the protected area represented only about 40 percent of the meadows' total area, according to a 1924 letter by Columbia National Forest Supervisor Adam Wright. His letter appears to be the final nail in the coffin of the five-year-old Yakima National Park proposal. Wright thought that if the last three-mile section of the Bird Creek Road were constructed, "a resort will, no doubt, be built in the [Bird Creek] Meadows under special use permit and all the conveniences necessary for the public will be installed."

The Portland climbing club Mazamas preferred the name Bird Creek Park for the area at the turn of the century, even though parts of it had become "almost a desert" because of grazing. To my knowledge, the first use of the name Bird Creek Meadows appeared in 1924 in a *Mazama* article about a successful round-the-mountain outing. The Mazamas made no mention of a possible "resort," and eighty years would pass until 2004, when a vastly

Glacial striations during the Ice Age characterize most of the dacite bedrock exposures in the meadows. This viewpoint overlooks Crooked Creek, the 2015 burn, and Glenwood Valley.

Near timberline, a herd of mountain goats heads upward toward the towering Little Ice Age moraine of Mazama Glacier.

Left: This aerial view of the Cougar Creek burn, Bird Lake, and Bird Creek Meadows was taken about a month after the fire, in mid-October 2015.
Right: The fire burned at high severity along the Bluff Lake Trail, killing nearly every tree, but many beargrass roots survived.

bigger resort would be proposed for the area encompassing Hellroaring Valley and Bird Creek Meadows.

United States Supreme Court Justice William O. Douglas called Bird Creek Meadows "a place of wonderment and worship." He had loved Mount Adams since he was a boy, and wrote eloquently about the mountain in two of his thirty-four books. Douglas wrote *My Wilderness* during his summer stays at his Glenwood cabin. I inherited and still use his massive Douglas fir desk upon which he penned the book.

Beginning his first season of living in Glenwood in 1958, Douglas had not seen the Bird Creek Meadows in more than thirty years. At that time the road ended at the base of Snowplow Mountain, and reaching the meadows, he wrote, was a "stiff hike." Douglas was dismayed when he and his wife Mercedes took their jeep on "a good dirt road" all the way to the eastern meadows at 6,000 feet. His "heart sank," he wrote, when he found twenty-seven cars ahead of them, adding that the sanctuary had been " . . . desecrated by the automobile." Douglas wrote that he was depressed afterward, that the "sacred precincts of a great mountain" had become accessible to " . . . potbellied men smoking black cigars, who never could climb a hundred feet." Bird Creek Meadows was no longer a wilderness.

A well-known champion for the preservation of wild places, Douglas felt that remoteness and the struggle to reach a pristine alpine lake or meadow were essential to the wellbeing of not only the individual, but of the American people. He was distressed that the subalpine areas of Mount Adams would be ruined by sheep, such as what he observed in the meadows on the northwest side of the Adams, also around 1958 or 1959. At the time, Bird Creek Meadows area was completely within the Gifford Pinchot National Forest, and part of it (within the Bird Creek Sheep and Goat Allotment) was still being grazed. In 1962 the Forest Service finally closed the sheep range, and the area was held in "rest condition." Douglas had probably written a strong letter of protest to the Chief of the Forest Service or the Secretary of Agriculture. It is also likely that the agency's higher management people were influenced by his *My Wilderness* book.

The Bird Creek Meadow Forest Camp was at the end of the road (now a trail) that Douglas was saddened to find. The large campground—a showpiece of the Forest Service—was our favorite place to sleep under the stars when Darvel and I were kids. A 1940 map shows the extensive trail system, including one planned to Shadow Lake and loop cutoffs. Our family and friends would frequently

Left: Old-growth mountain hemlock thrive near the start of the Round-the-Mountain Trail and Hellroaring Ridge area. Most survived the 2015 fire.
Right: A volunteer crew with Washington Trails Association rebuilds the Bluff Lake Trail in September 2017.

hike the area. The best six-mile loop hike doesn't exist anymore, unless you go off-trail. The missing link is a two-mile section that was called "Snowfields Trail." It headed north from the Round-the-Mountain Trail about a mile west of the old campground, and met the Hellroaring Ridge Trail near the edge of the big permanent snowfield at seventy-three hundred feet. Here stunted whitebark pines battle the elements, and patches of alpine tundra give way to the towering moraines below Mazama Glacier.

In 1972, when the Yakama Nation took over the area, the last three-quarters of a mile of the road to Bird Creek Meadows was converted to a section of the Round-the-Mountain Trail. Much of the old campground at the end of the road burned in the 2015 Cold Springs Fire. Even though the Tribe called it a "picnic area," very few people actually picnicked there over the last four decades. The wooden legs of the old massive tables rotted away years ago.

I'm not sure if William O. Douglas knew about the road shortening. My last contact with the Justice was in 1971, when my wife Susan and I visited him in his Supreme Court chambers. We talked mostly about Mount Adams and our new Wilderness Institute program. Douglas had not been on the mountain since 1963, the year he moved away from Glenwood after his divorce from Mercedes.

Fortunately, the 2015 Cougar Creek Fire spared all but a portion of the easternmost Bird Creek Meadows; but the fire destroyed the Mirror Lake Campground and most of the campsites at Bird Lake. The much larger campground at Bench Lake escaped completely. At this writing, public access into the Yakama Nation Mount Adams Recreation Area is closed indefinitely.

In August 2017, the Yakama Nation allowed the Washington Trails Association (WTA) to establish base camps at Bird Lake to conduct major trail repair work in the area. The Friends of Mount Adams, a non-profit group started in 2004, were partners in the WTA trail-maintenance project. On the last day of the project, Darvel and I drove to Bird Lake to check out the wonderful work that the volunteers had accomplished. Substantial repairs and improvements were made to Bird Lake, Bluff Lake, and Round-the-Mountain Trails, and also part of Trail of the Flowers.

Cattle trespass was extensive in Bird Creek Meadows during the 2016 and 2017 seasons, and impacts from grazing were severe. I pen these words in early 2018 with a hopeful heart for cattle-free subalpine areas on the south and southeast flanks of Mount Adams.

A September sunrise brings light into the Hellroaring Valley and illuminates the southeast face of Mount Adams.

Chapter 17

Wilderness Ramblings

High meadows . . . gnarled trees in wind-blown point . . . sunsets and sunrises over glacial peaks—
all these are bits of the wilderness we still possess. They give us retreat from the din of civilization;
they are places where we can get rid of the tensions of modern life.

— William O. Douglas

In 2014, on the fiftieth anniversary of the 1964 Wilderness Act, a Tacoma reporter asked Darvel and me what the Mount Adams Wilderness meant to us. He wanted a short answer. And so, like the inspirational words of Justice Douglas, we stressed the significance of Mount Adams as a quiet, beautiful refuge that for so many years has sustained our physical, mental, and spiritual health.

My brother and I have found endless joy in rambling and climbing in the remotest parts of the present-day 47,122-acre Mount Adams Wilderness. We've always enjoyed the mountain's challenges, like climbing its icefalls, navigating with a compass in white-out storms, crossing big glacial streams with no bridges, and finding hidden tarns. Since boyhood we've preferred to explore off-trail. Never with a GPS device. Even on our most recent backpacks, we've stumbled upon sublime, flower-filled meadows and viewpoints that we never knew existed. Occasionally we disagree mildly on which route to take, but it's an issue that hardly ever matters. We love the silence, the whispering breezes, the whistling marmot, the haunting, two-note trills of the varied thrush that always seem to be hidden in the upper layers of the montane forest.

The Forest Service trail system is excellent and allows many choices to traverse both forested areas and the subalpine zone. The latest Mount Adams Wilderness Map (2015), guidebooks, and online information provide readily available guidance and rules for use. In the past few decades, the Pacific Crest Trail has become quite crowded during the high season, and trampling is killing more and more vegetation in places like Killen Creek and High Camp.

Darvel and I love the companionship of a few good friends to share our wilderness experience. Among my favorite memories, our dear friend (and birder) "HC" Tupper accompanied me for a late-season, off-trail backpack. During the three-day trip in September 2013, he identified eighteen bird species between the Divide Camp Trailhead and Red Butte on the northeast side. It would be HC's last backpack on Mount Adams; he died of cancer two years later. His love for the mountain was profound, and I still have his bird list and notes from that September 11: "hairy woodpecker, Clark's nutcracker, raven, crow, chipping sparrow, dark-eyed juncos, yellow-rumped warbler, Townsend's solitaire, sharp-skinned hawk, red-tailed hawk, mountain chickadee, golden-crowned kinglet, northern flicker, Vaux's swifts, red-breasted nuthatch, hermit warbler, ruffed grouse, gray-crowned rosy finch (*good bird*)."

I haven't spotted the elusive white-tailed ptarmigan in the Mount Adams Wilderness for many years. It is the smallest member of the grouse family, and long ago we would hear its piercing calls at night in areas of alpine tundra. I'll never forget the ptarmigan hen on her nest in a tundra meadow near Red Butte. It was in the late 1970s, and the hen was sitting on six eggs. That night we experienced a fearsome thunderstorm with lightning strikes too close for comfort. The next morning, the mother hen was tending five tiny ptarmigan chicks (one egg didn't hatch). We spent only an amazing moment or two at the spot,

A lovely lake on the west side of Adams lies hidden in the subalpine life zone. *Below:* Surrounded by burned forest in 2013, Grassy Hill emerges luxuriant with penstemon and fritillary butterflies.

allowing the new ptarmigan family to scurry to a better hiding place from raptors.

Our favorite off-trail rambles are in the less-traveled alpine life zone—from timberline to the bases of the steep moraines. It's a harsh environment and most vegetation in the alpine is reduced to dwarf status. Tree line averages around the 7,000-foot level, but elevations vary depending on steep Little Ice Age moraines and blocky, young lava flows. The uppermost limit of trees is about 8,500 feet. Gnarled and twisted trees called krummholz (German for "crooked wood") are pruned by the freezing gales of winter. Whitebark pine are the heartiest of the few stunted conifer species that grow in the alpine zone. They survive with the protection of boulders, drifted snow, and islands of other dwarf trees, mainly subalpine fir and mountain hemlock. Branches that poke up too

Top: With a view of Mount Rainier, Darvel enjoys morning coffee at a beautiful camp. *Left:* Morning is a great time to ramble leisurely above timberline, and to pursue photography before light becomes too harsh. *Right:* I'm always shooting glaciers to record not only their beauty, but to document significant change on the mountain through the decades. (Hugh McMahan)

Top: Always on the move, a herd of mountain goats browses the grasses and sedges of alpine tundra. *Left:* A young ruffed grouse remained unruffled on a limb of a whitebark pine. *Right:* A battle-scarred whitebark pine has been clinging to life on the northeast side for centuries. I've photographed the same tree many times.

Susan Saul ascends alpine tundra on a typical August morning in 2007.

Alpine tundra flowers in this photo includes low mountain lupine, woolly pussytoes, Thompson's paintbrush, sandwort, and small-flowered penstemon. *Below:* In 2004, a short-fruited smelowskia patch at 11,000 feet on Suksdorf Ridge was later confirmed as the highest-growing plant in Washington state.

high usually die. Toward the uppermost tree limit, ghostly skeletons of dead whitebarks dot the barren landscape, thus the appropriateness of their name. The whitebark krummholz sometimes migrate downwind in rows about as high as a grown man. The rows and islands of the dense trees have provided welcome shelter on cold, windy days.

Warming climate and reduced snowpacks are causing plants to colonize ever higher on the mountain. Botanist Paul Slichter saw sedges, alpine grasses, and forbs as high as 9,500 feet between the large moraines of Adams Glacier. In 2004 on Suksdorf Ridge, I found a healthy patch of flowering short-fruited smelowskia at 11,000 feet. It was confirmed as the highest-growing plant in Washington State. Slichter discovered a two-foot-high *black cottonwood* at 7,000 feet, which must be a record. Alpine willows are numerous at that level and seem to be increasing in numbers.

Some of the most common ground-hugging flowers that I notice in the alpine zone are low mountain lupine, woolly pussytoes, partridgefoot, white and pink mountain heather, magenta paintbrush, Thompson's paintbrush, sandwort, and spreading phlox. In 2010, Slichter documented sixty-one plant species in the alpine areas on the northwest north side of Mount Adams. Tundra plants

At sunset, the northwest face and Adams Glacier presents an irresistible photo opportunity in August 2013. *Below:* A lupine meadow at timberline is backlit as the sun sets through the hazy skies of mid-summer.

On a moonless and dark night, the center of the Milky Way seems to glow in muted hues, while a satellite passes at upper right.

are very fragile and are easily killed by foot traffic, so I advise people to step carefully and spread out, so as to not create human trails. Also, camping should always be avoided in a flowered meadow.

Among the alpine flowers are sedges and grasses that mountain goats depend on. I've seen herds of more than twenty goats hanging out on open slopes, where they can easily spot predators. When people are around, they move quickly to safe distances. As on the east side, numbers of goats seem to be increasing, and they are spreading into areas where I have never seen them before, like Horseshoe Meadow.

Change is a constant, especially in the atmosphere and and the increasing difficulty of finding really dark skies. As distant horizons become increasingly smoky and hazy, and in the absence of high clouds, sunrises and sunsets are certainly more intense. I'm not sure about redder suns when wildfires are finally extinguished. But the high country on the northern flanks of Mount Adams is best for viewing the deep night sky on a cloudless night, regardless of season.

For me, nothing in the developed world can compare with watching an August sunset from a lupine-filled meadow at tree line, then seeing the northwest face of Mount Adams slowly turn red in alpenglow. I remember one hushed, moonless night, when the night sky finally darkened, and I gazed upward toward the mottled core of our Milky Way galaxy, home of about a hundred billion stars. It was an awe-inspiring evening, a time to be at utter peace with myself and the world.

Darvel and I will always have our favorite areas in the wilderness high country, of course, but we'd prefer not to share their locations publicly, except through these images. Exploration and self-discovery are the great rewards of the freedom to wander and ramble.

Chapter 18

Protecting the Mountain

We simply need that wild country available to us, even if we never do more than drive to its edge and look in. For it can be a means of reassuring ourselves of our sanity as creatures, a part of the geography of hope.

— Wallace Stegner

In fall 2004, the Mount Hood Meadows Development Corporation proposed a massive four-season resort on Mount Adams' gorgeous southeast flanks, all within the Yakama Nation's Tract D. Called an "eco-resort," it would have covered 11,000 acres or 17 square miles. The scheme included 2,500 housing units (centered in Hellroaring Meadow), a casino and "village," eight chairlifts, gondola, and tram to 11,000 feet, three eighteen-hole golf courses, and so on. A mega resort city would occupy the Bird Lake–Bird Creek Meadows area, Ridge of Wonders, Mazama Glacier, all of Hellroaring Valley, and considerable montane forestlands (now partially burned).

Horrified, I dropped everything and went to work, first making an overlay graphic that showed the whole area. Then I began daily email reports to friends and everyone else I could think of. People who responded were aghast, and my email list quickly grew to several hundred. We soon established Friends of Mount Adams (FOMA), and advocated for the mountain's protection in a low-keyed, respectful way—such as a letter to the editor of the *Yakama Nation Review*. However, it seemed that most members of the Tribe were opposed to the plan from the very beginning. In late November 2004, the Yakama Tribal Council rejected the resort proposal. One Tribal Council member said, "We do not want to sacrifice an area of extreme cultural importance to the Tribe."

As a 501(c)3 non-profit organization, FOMA has a volunteer board but no actual membership, although I send occasional informational email reports to a list that has grown to about eight hundred. Overall, the FOMA board

and I have been supportive of both the Yakama Nation and Forest Service stewardship of Mount Adams.

Finding the balance between human enjoyment and protection, Darvel and I, along with other FOMA board members, led annual hikes on different sides of the mountain between 2006 and 2016. The hikes were always filled to capacity. Increasing numbers of people want to find new areas of high country to explore. But they also want to learn and understand the land and the history of the area they walk through. From 2011 through 2015, capacity audiences attended the annual Friends-sponsored, science-based conferences and educational forums held in Trout Lake and White Salmon, Washington. We partnered with the Yakama Nation and Forest Service on these events.

Cattle trespass in the subalpine meadows of the south and southeast sides of Mount Adams is one of the most important issues that FOMA has faced in the past decade. It has been an on-again, off-again problem, and FOMA's role has been mostly documentation and getting stakeholders together to share information and concerns. The Forest Service and Yakama Nation, as well as cattle-owner permittees, made good-faith efforts to keep fences up and cattle out, but not always successfully.

The 2015 Cougar Creek Fire heavily impacted roads, recreation facilities, and trails, and also destroyed cattle drift fences. Because of limited funding, short staffing, and priority to get forested stands reforested, the Yakama Nation drift fence has not been rebuilt since the fire. This has allowed widespread cattle trespass into Bird Creek Meadows.

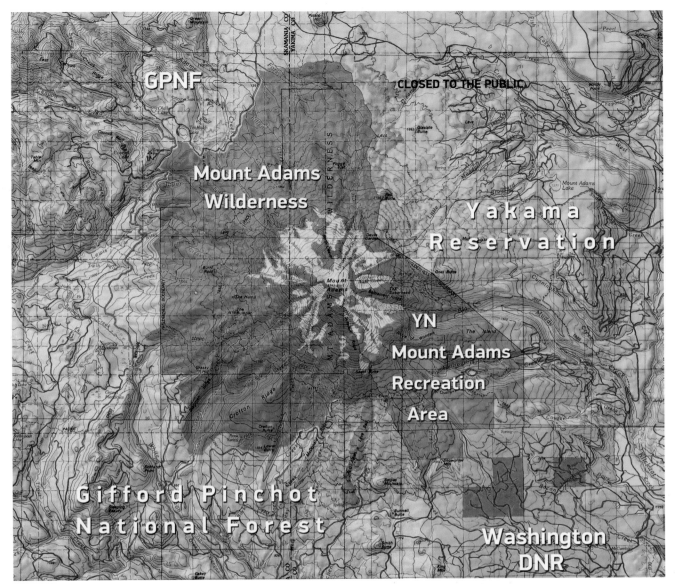

The Mount Adams volcano is divided and managed by three governmental agencies—Gifford Pinchot National Forest, the Yakama Nation, and Washington Department of Natural Resources—as well as a few private landowners on its southern flanks.

At this point, I must take the long view and be optimistic. Everyone takes seriously the stewardship of the beloved subalpine meadows in both Gifford Pinchot National Forest and Yakama Reservation. Proper fences will be built and maintained. The meadows eventually will recover from cattle damage, but it will be a long process. Volunteer assistance may be required to help it along, such as scattering cow pies that are on or near trails. Cow pies biodegrade very slowly; it takes decades at that elevation. Perhaps a botanist will make recommendations on how humans can assist in restoration, such as replanting native

vegetation in some of the most impacted areas. In the end though, nature heals itself in grand fashion.

Snowmobiling is prohibited within all Yakama Nation lands, but trespass into the Recreation Area has been common during winter and spring months, and enforcement of the closure minimal. There are signs of change, though. The Yakama Nation manages its lands consistent with its Natural Resources Policy Plan and Forest Management Plan to protect its natural resources, especially the habitat of sensitive species such as mountain goats, white-tailed ptarmigan, red fox, and the extremely rare wolverine. In

Friends of Mount Adams volunteers in 2011 roll up and haul out abandoned drift-fence wire near Gotchen Creek Meadows in Gifford Pinchot National Forest.

the meantime, "sledders" regularly traverse Bird Creek Meadows and some zoom up to Mazama Glacier for daring "high marking" on the glacier headwall. A few venture on to Mount Adams' summit, which means they would also penetrate the uppermost part of Mount Adams Wilderness. The steep sides of Hellroaring Canyon are also popular with the sledders.

Snowmobiles are especially harmful, because they can leak gas and oil into the snowpack (including snow- and ice-covered lakes), damage young trees and shrubs, cause erosion and ruts, and spread broken parts across the landscape. Snowmobiling on the tribe's sacred Pahto violates Yakama Nation laws and shows disrespect to the members' religious and cultural beliefs.

Looking ahead, Yakama Nation wildlife biologist Mark Nuetzmann may embark on an excellent plan for an eighteen-month "Alpine Ecosystem Protection Project." It would focus on two areas: the decrease of key sensitive plant and animal species, and the long-standing snowmobile trespass problem. FOMA would be a partner in the project. As of this writing, Nuetzmann doesn't know if his proposal will find funding through a U.S. Fish and Wildlife Service Wildlife Grant program. Nothing could be more important for the future of the Yakamas' side of Mount Adams.

Understanding the decline in certain wildlife populations is the focus of FOMA board member and biologist Jocelyn Akins, research director of the Cascades Carnivore Project. Researchers are studying how environmental changes in the western mountains affect the conservation of rare mountain carnivores. In a FOMA-sponsored event in November 2017, Akins spoke about her dissertation work on the Cascade red fox of Mount Adams. The rare carnivore is a subspecies of red fox that lives year-round in high-elevation forests and subalpine parklands. It forages for small mammals and snowshoe hare in alpine meadows and copses of whitebark pine, subalpine fir, and mountain hemlock. Like most furbearers over the last century, it has suffered significant declines due to fur trapping and predator-control programs. Yet despite the removal of these threats, the Cascade red fox continues to decline, perhaps due to shrinking high-elevation parkland

Left: Trespassing cattle occupy Bird Creek Meadows in September 2017. *Right:* Cattle adversely impact wetlands in the meadows, as well as eat plants like Lewis monkeyflowers.

and meadows from climate change, or the expansion of coyotes into the high-elevation habitats.

There is a delicate balance in the natural world that seems so hardy yet sometimes is so easily broken. The balance is altered by both human causes, including climate change, and natural events such as wildfires. To understand what is happening on Mount Adams and other wild areas, scientific research is more important now than ever before. And so is the role of stewardship in the here and now. I always hope for rolling back some of the harm that humans have done. Over the past seven decades, Darvel and I are blessed to have observed and, in many ways, documented a dazzling array of changes on Mount Adams. Even partially comprehending the changes has been an experience of a lifetime.

Our love for Mount Adams was illuminated in an Oregon Public Broadcasting television program, *Oregon Field Guide*, in February 2018. We were featured in an eight-minute segment produced by Sarah Fox of Hood River and titled "Lloyd Brothers of Mount Adams." Darvel's and my years are now numbered for anything but moderate trail hikes on the mountain, but we will never give up our elder roles as its advocates, educators, and celebrants.

The advice I give now: Discover Mount Adams on your own, but be careful of your impact. Future generations will want to make their own discoveries of an undisturbed mountain wonderland.

Snowmobile trespass in the Yakama Nation Recreation Area is a longstanding and serious issue. *Below:* A snowmobile windshield creates a small waterfall in a Bird Creek Meadows stream.

Quaking aspens at the edge of Camas Prairie provide a serene, late-fall scene of Mount Adams' south face.

Selected References

Ballou, Robert. 1938. *Early Klickitat Valley Days*. Goldendale, WA: The Goldendale Sentinel.

Becky, Fred. 1987. *Cascade Alpine Guide, Climbing and High Routes: Columbia River to Stevens Pass*, 53-68. Seattle: The Mountaineers.

Biek, David, and Susan McDougall. 2007. *The Flora of Mount Adams, Washington*, 5-24. Seattle: Sound Books.

Briley, Ann. 1986. *Lonely Pedestrian: Francis Marion Streamer*. Fairfield, WA: Ye Galleon Press.

Byam, F. M. "The Mount Adams Slide of 1921." *Mazama* 6, no. 2.

Charley, Jobe. Undated PDF online. "The Legend of Mount Adams." Washington State Historical Society. http:// washingtonhistory.org/files/library/legendofmtadams.pdf

Douglas, William O. 1950. *Of Men and Mountains*, 292-312. New York: Harper & Brothers.

——. (1960) 1968. *My Wilderness: The Pacific West*, 61-80. New York: Pyramid Publications.

Hildreth, Wes, and Judy Fierstein. 1995. *Geologic Map of the Mount Adams Volcanic Field, Cascade Range of Southern Washington*. U. S. Geological Survey Map I-2460.

——. 1997. "Recent Eruptions of Mountain Adams, Washington, USA." *Bulletin of Volcanology* 58.

Hunt, John Clark, 1968. "Mt. Adams Lookout Proved Too Tough for Man to Take," *Oregon Journal*, August 20, 1968.

Karlsson, Erick, and Keith McCoy. 1965. "Adams' Mountain Men," 8-14. *The Mountaineer* 58 no. 4 (March 15).

Kirk, Ruth, and Richard Daugherty. 2007. *Archaeology in Washington*. Seattle: University of Washington Press.

Lyman, William D. 1896. "The Glaciers of Mount Adams," 98-101. *Mazama* 1.

——. 1902. "Mount Adams Outing, 1902," 168. *Mazama*.

Mack, Cheryl A. 2003. "A burning issue: American Indian fire use on the Mt. Rainier Forest Reserve," 20-24. *Fire Management Today*. 63 no. 2.

Mack, Cheryl A., and Richard McClure. 2002. "Vaccinium Processing in the Washington Cascades," 24-60. *Journal of Ethnobiology* 22 no. 1.

McClure, Rick and Cheryl Mack. 2008. *For the Greatest Good: Early History of Gifford Pinchot National Forest*. Seattle: Northwest Interpretive Association.

McCoy, Keith. 1987. *The Mount Adams Country: Forgotten Corner of the Columbia River Gorge*, 171-180. White Salmon, WA: Pahto Publications.

McDougall, Susan. 2005. *The Wildflowers of Mount Adams, Washington*. Tacoma: Sound Books.

Phillips, Kenneth N. 1941. "Fumaroles of Mount St. Helens and Mount Adams," 37-42. *Mazama* 23 no 12.

Reid, Harry F. 1906. "Studies of Glaciers of Mount Hood and Mount Adams," 113-132. *Zeitschrift fur Gletscherkunde*.

Rusk, C. E. 1919. *Mount Adams: Towering Sentinel of the Lower Columbia Basin—Reasons for it Preservation & Maintenance as a National Park*. Yakima: Yakima Commercial Club.

——. 1978. *Tales of a Western Mountaineer: With a Portrait of C. E. Rusk by Darryl Lloyd*. Seattle: The Mountaineers.

Rusk, Claude Ewing. 1946. "The Wonderful Story of Abe Lincoln." *The American Alpine Journal*, 48-53. Special War Number. New York: The American Alpine Club.

Scott, William E., Richard M. Iverson, James W. Vallance, and Wes Hildreth. 1995. *Volcano Hazards in the Mount Adams Region, Washington*. U.S. Geological Survey Open-File Report 95-492.

Sitts, Danielle J., Andrew. G. Fountain and Matthew J. Hoffman. 2010. "Twentieth Century Glacier Change on Mount Adams, Washington, USA," 378-385. *Northwest Science* 84.

Topinka, Lyn. 2017 online. "Mount Adams, Washington: Lewis & Clark's Columbia River – 200 Years Later." http:// columbiariverimages.com/Regions/Places/mount_adams .html

Vallance, James W. 1997. "Postglacial Lahars and Potential Hazards in the White Salmon River System on the Southwest Flank of Mount Adams, Washington." *U.S. Geological Survey Bulletin* 2161.

Weber, William A. 1944. *The Botanical Collections of Wilhelm N. Suksdorf*, 117-118. Research Studies, State College of Washington 12.

Williams, John H. 1912. *The Guardians of the Columbia: Mount Hood, Mount Adams and Mount St. Helens*, 89-104. Tacoma: John H. Williams.

Wuerthner, George. 2006. *The Wildfire Reader: A Century of Failed Forest Policy*. Washington: Island Press.

An intense aurora in June 2013 reflects vivid hues of green and purple on Trout Lake. (Darlisa Black)

Index

Adams' summit icecap drapes over the Rusk Glacier headwall on the east face.